TA 683 FEL

20 0024867 5   TELEPEN

KING'S

D0228935

DATE DUE FOR RETURN

ACCESSION
CANCELLED

0 7 MAY 1999

WITHDRAWN
FROM STOCK
QMUL LIBRARY

Lessons from Failures of Concrete Structures

AMERICAN CONCRETE INSTITUTE MONOGRAPH SERIES

Lessons from Failures of Concrete Structures

JACOB FELD

PUBLISHED JOINTLY BY

AMERICAN CONCRETE INSTITUTE
DETROIT, MICHIGAN
THE IOWA STATE UNIVERSITY PRESS
AMES, IOWA

64522

TA683.F46

Civil Engineering

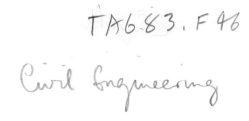

ACI Monograph No. 1

This monograph is published in furtherance of ACI objectives in the fields of engineering education and technology. The Institute is not responsible, as a body, for the statements and opinions advanced in this publication; Institute authority attaches only to standards adopted as provided in the ACI Bylaws.

Copyright © 1964 American Concrete Institute
P.O. Box 4754, Redford Station
Detroit, Michigan 48219
Manufactured in the United States of America
Second printing, 1965

Library of Congress Catalog Card Number: 64-23942

QMW LIBRARY
(MILE END)

Foreword

SINCE ITS FOUNDING in 1905, one of the primary objectives of the American Concrete Institute has been to gather and disseminate information about the properties and uses of plain and reinforced concrete and their constituent materials.

ACI Committee 103, Monographs, was organized to expedite the dissemination of knowledge in specialized areas of the concrete field through publication of a series of monographs. The committee, which began as a task group of the Technical Activities Committee in 1960, was officially designated Committee 103 in 1963. It is anticipated that monograph manuscripts will be prepared by highly qualified authorities in the several fields to be treated. Technical content of the monographs will reflect the thinking and experience of the writers, and not necessarily that of Committee 103.

Each monograph within the series will develop a thorough understanding of the subject and will summarize the principal elements of what should be known about a specific subject to use concrete to best advantage. Free from the space limitations necessary for an ACI JOURNAL paper, the monograph writers will be able to provide a more thorough and complete treatment of their subject.

These monographs are tailored neither for the uninformed layman nor for the well-informed few. Rather it is intended that these publications be of maximum value to the practicing engineer, contractor, advanced student, and others having a working knowledge of concrete and its properties.

The first manuscript in this continuing series is on a subject of unusually broad interest. It comes at a time when the building industry is expanding at an increasing rate and is looking to the past for lessons and to the future for greater progress.

In the preparation of this monograph Committee 103 and the author wish to give special acknowledgment to M. K. Hurd for the editorial treatment and to Robert C. Baldwin for literature research on the examples presented.

ACI COMMITTEE 103

Contents

ABOUT THE AUTHOR

DIAGNOSIS OF AILING AND FAILING STRUCTURES has been both vocation and avocation for New York consulting engineer Jacob Feld for the past 40 years. Dr. Feld's preoccupation with failures and the lessons to be learned from them dates back to 1924 when he was designing walls and abutments for the Long Island Railroad, and some of these early experiences are recounted in the present text. Since then he has gained an international reputation as an authority on structural failure as he has continued to observe, analyze, and criticize building industry practices.

Since establishing his engineering office in 1926, Dr. Feld has advised clients on and investigated a wide range of structural failures—sagging slabs, sinking foundations, defective piles, corroded reinforcement, and cracking plaster, to mention only a few. His clients have been owners, architects, engineers, contractors, financiers, insurance companies, and municipalities. He has also acted as special consultant to the U. S. Air Force.

Dr. Feld's concern with failing structures has been paralleled by a distinguished personal success in the field of structural design. His design and construction commissions have included more than 50 flat plate reinforced concrete apartment houses and office buildings, as well as part of the Sixth Avenue Subway in New York; the Naval Ammunition Depot in Earle, N. J.; Stewart Airfield at West Point, N. Y.; and the Sampson Naval Training Station at Geneva, N. Y. More recently he prepared the structural design for the New York Coliseum and the Guggenheim Museum, also in New York.

A native of Austria, Dr. Feld received his engineering education at the College of the City of New York and at the University of Cincinnati, where he earned his doctorate in 1922. A long-time member of the American Concrete Institute and Fellow of the American Society of Civil Engineers, he has been active in the committee work of these organizations, has written many scientific and technical papers for their journals as well as for other American, German, and Australian periodicals. In 1963, Dr. Feld received the French Order of Merit in Research and Invention.

Lessons from Failures of Concrete Structures

1

Introduction

THE RESULTS OF ENGINEERING DESIGN too often fail to agree with the
desires or purposes of the designer. No cures can be developed or
preventive rules standardized unless information on what has caused
prior failure is made known. From the early history of the construction industry, even today in the 1960's, there has been a need to warn
the uninitiated, the careless, and the optimistic designers and builders
that lessons can be learned from the unsuccessful designs of their
predecessors and their colleagues. That such lessons are often not
learned is a sorry fact, owing at least in part to the inadequate publication of the full accounts of failures. Scanty and sketchy reports of
failures, including the sensational headlines of the public press are
only a part of the record. It is hoped that this monograph will supply
some of the missing information, and make more obvious the lessons
that can be gleaned from it.

The author has long felt that one of the worst indictments against
the professions is the statement: "Doctors bury their mistakes, architects cover them with ivy, and engineers write long reports which
never see the light of day." However, there is a certain amount of
professional precedent for publishing reports of unsuccessful incidents. Medical journals describe in detail diagnoses and treatments
which did not result in a successful cure. Legal tomes give the arguments on both sides of a case in which exactly half the litigants did

1

not win. Scientific literature abounds with reports of research ending in blind alleys with no positive results; these are valuable warnings of what directions are nonproductive.

The purpose of this monograph is to similarly serve the engineering profession and construction industry by bringing to light some oft repeated errors in judgment, in design, in detail, in control, and in performance. Except where other authorities are specifically cited, the opinions expressed are those of the author, who has undertaken to voice them in the hope and belief that full knowledge and understanding of such experiences will reduce the number of failures of concrete structures. This is not an easy account to write . . . nor is the morbid accounting of accidents a pleasurable task. It is hoped that no one will take the matters or incidents reported herein as a personal slight, that the writer will lose no friends from his statements, and that the reader may gain by the reported experience of others.

Since publication of the monograph has been sponsored by the American Concrete Institute, the cases and examples presented have been chosen almost entirely from the field of concrete structures and the formwork or processes required to build them. This focusing on concrete structures in no way is to be construed that failures are a natural consequence of the use of concrete. Failures occur in all types of structures, minimal and monumental alike, whether framed or wall bearing, whether with timber, steel, or concrete as the basic supporting material. Similar, and in many phases more lengthy, reports are possible on the subject of timber and steel structures, not to mention foundations, dams, and other earth structures. It is to be hoped that technical societies in other fields of construction and design will publish similar accounts of failures in their own fields and thus contribute to the gradual reduction of failures in all areas of construction.

FAILURES DEFINED

If we define engineering failure as observed collapse, there are comparatively few failures. On the other hand, if nonconformity with design expectations is engineering failure, and if one takes the trouble to measure the shape, position, and condition of completed structures, there are many failures. This is more true in the complicated space frames than in the simple or pin-connected structures. Unwanted settlements, sometimes unexplainable deformations, are often found, and it is questioned whether they are failures, or normal but unexpected strains, or merely "incidents," to use a European term to describe the unexpected results. Whether failure or not, there frequently follows

Figure 1.1—If one takes time to measure the **shape, position,** and **condition** of completed structures, many failures to comply with good design and construction practice will be found. Here, the construction joint on the column is improperly placed with respect to the girder it supports, and there is severe honeycombing at the juncture of column and girder. The same defect appears in the next column (lower right).

long, expensive litigation where the experts are quizzed by their clients' lawyers and cross-examined at great length by the opponents' counsel in an attempt to pin down the "proximate" cause of the failure or incident.

The legal fiction that responsibility stems from a single and only cause does not make it possible to determine such cause either by observation or deduction. Sometimes there is a single explanation for a failure; more often there is a combination of conditions—mistakes, oversights, misunderstandings, even dishonest performance—where no single item can be picked as the sole and only cause of failure. Yet each one in a way may be the responsible straw that broke the camel's back; if just one of the straws had not been added, the camel's back would have remained unbroken.

While recognizing that there is rarely a single cause for a failure, it is nonetheless helpful for purposes of discussion to group cases in a general way according to probable causes. The following general categories of failure causes have been used in preparing the monograph:

Design deficiencies
Problems during construction, with special attention to formwork
Problems of durability and compatibility of materials
Problems relating to foundations and other particular types of structures.

Where several factors clearly have contributed to failure, the case has been placed in the category that seemed most significant; admittedly some arbitrary assignments have been necessary.

Failures discussed within this general framework include cases of collapse, total or partial, either during construction or during the service life of the structure (fortunately collapses are much more common during construction than after completion and full occupancy). Cracking, spalling, and surface disintegration which either destroys the desired appearance or usability, as well as disintegration which leads to or is a part of collapse, are included among the cases. Deflection which is so large as to impair the function for which a structure was intended and general weakness of a structure—such as failure of materials to measure up to specified design strength—also constitute failure in terms of the inability to meet designer's standards. The latter is more difficult to establish, since reserve strength provided by a factor of safety in the design many times masks such a weakness.

This monograph makes no attempt to list all failures, or all of any one type of failure; such a purpose would require a publication of encyclopedic scope. Rather certain outstanding incidents and many typical failures have been chosen in an effort to clarify the lessons that can be learned from them. Many readers will be suprised to find omission of cases well known to them. It is their duty to publicize their knowledge. By increasing the number of examples, with a detailed description of probable causes if possible, they will render a real service to the profession. The published record shows that no area, no branch of the industry, no type of design office, whether large or small, public or private, is immune to the occurrence of failures in the end product.

INVESTIGATION OF FAILURES

Where loss of life is involved in a structural failure, a coroner's investigation is undertaken, and the testimony of expert witnesses is

Figure 1.2—"Funnel of failure" is apparent in the debris of this structure where one poor footing triggered the collapse of a four-story building.

sought, in an effort to establish whether criminal action should be instituted. Financially interested parties frequently organize their own investigations of failures to establish evidence on which to base civil suits. Too often the findings are ambiguously stated, biased or otherwise of doubtful reliability; for example, take the case of the collapse of a concrete building in Petrograd, Russia, in 1903.[1]* A commission was appointed to investigate the causes and made its report. Because of some dissatisfaction, a second commission was appointed, which conclusively disproved the conclusions of the first commission and gave the following as principal causes of failure: (1) The design, both system used and computations, was incorrect; but the chief causes were: (2) poor

---

* All references are listed at the end of the text, p. 161.

cement and concrete; and (3) lack of superintendence. How much reliance can be given to such a report! Fortunately not all investigations are so unproductive of lessons learned, as some of the cases in this monograph demonstrate.

In the course of many years of study of structural failures, both as a vocation and as an avocation, the author has observed a phenomenon described as "funnels of failure" which may be useful to others in their studies. Careful observation of collapsed structures, especially before any disturbance of the debris, and sometimes necessarily from an elevated position on a nearby structure or even from a helicopter, will show a definite pattern of successive movement.* Gravity of course pulls vertically, but the obstruction of parts that do not go in the initial fall introduces lateral resistance to the free fall. As a result a wedge or funnel shape is frequently noted in the debris. The axis points to the location of the initial failure. Where determination of the "proximate" cause is a necessity or where technical information of the cause is desired, an early inspection is advisable. In lieu thereof, close study of early photographs is of value. In one case of the partial collapse of a four-story concrete building, a small scale model made of the collapsed portion, when suspended in inverted position, was found to hang with floors level from a column which was noted by aerial observation to be the axis of the funnel of failure. Omission of the footing under this column was definitely the triggering cause of the failure (see also foundations, p. 135).

PROFESSIONAL RESPONSIBILITY

Engineering work taken as the sum total of project concept, choice of materials, structural design, production of materials, erection of the components and even final cleanup and equipment installation always involves the interrelated requirements of sufficiency and necessity. A "sufficient" structure is one that is safe, not only from collapse but also from undue deterioration or deflection. Necessity, as a measure or control of economy, should only be considered after safe conditions have been established. Continous pressure for greater economy, from private financial competition as well as from public demand that bud-

---

* T. L. Condron, commenting on the 1911 failure of the Prestolite Building in Indianapolis, remarked on this phenomenon. "As stated by an engineer who examined the wreck a few hours after the collapse . . . falsework posts remained in a nearly vertical position, as if the floor supporting them had collapsed and let the structure above go down as through a funnel." (*Engineering News,* V. 67, No. 2, Jan. 11, 1912, p. 69.)

gets must be met even if unreasonable in both engineering design and construction schedules, has too often resulted in safety reduced to just below the minimum sufficiency. Failure of a part or even serious collapse of the whole structure occurs almost always during construction when the latent uncalculated space frame strengths have not yet been provided. The boundary between stability and instability, between sufficiency and failure, is only the dimension of a thin hair. Ignorance of the boundary is no excuse when a failure occurs.

Much more emphasis in technical education must be placed on what not to do and when to say "no," rather than to give the impression in the untutored and inexperienced mind that blind compliance with minimal code provisions and reports of committees signed by all the members after several years disagreement (but with ultimate consent to the strongest minority) is a guarantee of sufficiency. Perhaps the technical societies should award annual prizes for complete descriptions and analyses of failures so that everyone can learn from those experiences to avoid similar trouble in his own practice.

Engineering if it is to assume full stature as a profession has a duty to record for the use and profit of present and future engineers the experiences which have not been successful, with as much information as can be gathered to explain wherein the laws of nature were violated and insufficient resistance was provided to internal and external forces. As Richard Humphrey remarked[2] to the National Association of Cement Users more than 50 years ago, "We should not be afraid to state the truth, even though it hurts; we should by all means be honest and not hold malice toward those who frankly call our attention to the . . . weaknesses" of concrete construction.

2

Historical References

ARCHAEOLOGY DEPENDS TO A LARGE EXTENT on the uncovered debris of engineering failures. If the Code of Hammurabi (about 1750 BC) is typical of ancient regulations, few engineer-builders under that jurisdiction had the opportunity to learn from their own mistakes. The five basic rules covering failures (Figure 2.1) are:[3]

> If a builder build a house for a man and do not make its construction firm and the house which he has built collapse and cause the death of the owner of the house—that builder shall be put to death.
> If it cause the death of the son of the owner of the house—they shall put to death a son of that builder.
> If it cause the death of a slave of the owner of the house—he shall give to the owner of the house a slave of equal value.
> If it destroy property, he shall restore whatever it destroyed, and because he did not make the house which he built firm and it collapsed, he shall rebuild the house which collapsed at his own expense.
> If a builder build a house for a man and do not make its construction meet the requirements and a wall fall in, that builder shall strengthen the wall at his own expense.

It is not known whether these rules stopped all failures, but they certainly must have discouraged shoddy construction and eliminated the possibility of repetitive malpractice.

9

History and fable report the summary execution in ancient civilizations of the designer-builders of sucessful monuments, as a guarantee that competing or superior structures would not be built. If these stories are true, there would have been an incentive to perform poorly and imperfectly.

Deep excavation into the layers of rubble at city sites shows that entire ancient city complexes collapsed from normal aging as well as from enemy attack at times. In the exploratory trenches dug at the walls of Jericho, Major Tollak, chief engineer of the Allenby invasion of Palestine in World War I, uncovered at least six distinct collapsed walls before coming to the wall which Joshua felled. Reportedly that

Figure 2.1—A copy of part of the original cuneiform inscription of the "building code" of Hammurabi which deals with failures. Note that the symbol for "builder" (first character in third line of left panel, and recurring throughout the text) resembles the framework of a house—a main center post with four corner posts all connected and braced by roof beams.

collapse was the first failure from sonic forces. However, Tollak asserted that the Jericho wall fell from the undermining of the foundation stones, operations being carried on by miners while the defenders were distracted by the blowing of horns.

In Greco-Roman times the construction industry was in the hands of trained slave artisans, and successful work was rewarded by gifts of substance as well as of freedom. With no competitive financial or time schedule to worry the builder, work was well done and with apparent great success. Similarly in the medieval period, time was no object, and the great successful religious and governmental structures have lasted for centuries. One wonders whether our modern works will exist for a comparable age.

Regarding construction, English common law, as found in fifteenth century court records, states "If a carpenter undertake to build a house and does it ill, an action will lie against him." The Napoleonic code, which is the basis of common law wherever the original settlers were French, places a greater responsibility on the designer and the professional in charge of the work. As agent of the owner, he is to safeguard the investment and guarantee proper and adequate performance, which is somewhat more than what was expected in English common law.

So, historically, the burden rests on the construction industry to see that work is done well. Each partner in the industry, from the architect to the project foreman, must lend every effort to avoid and eliminate every possible cause of "ill" structures.

EARLY PROBLEMS IN CONSTRUCTION

In the period from 1870 to 1900, construction became a large industry in the United States, under the influence of an expanding transportation system and a rising industrial economy. Comparatively little was recorded at that time of failures in buildings, most of which were heavy masonry wall-bearing structures with good timber floors. Bridge spans, however, soon exceeded the capacity of timber trusses, and a great competition in the sale of iron spans developed.

Since knowledge relating to construction of these bridges was largely in the hands of the contractor, it was then customary for him to submit bridge bids based on his own plans and specifications. Frequent and spectacular failures were directly attributable to this practice. Such failures made newspaper headlines almost daily. Foreign technical journals commented on the great number of unsuccessful designs for bridges in the United States.

Engineering magazines from 1875 to 1895 were as full of reports of railroad accidents and bridge failures as today's daily newspapers are of automobile traffic accidents. Even as late as 1905 the weekly news summary in *Engineering Record* describes the most serious railroad wreck of the week, usually tied in with a bridge failure. C. F. Stowell[4] published a series of discouraging accounts of iron bridge failures resulting from railway traffic, totaling 502 cases in the period from 1878 to 1895.* These reports received wide publicity and attention and must have influenced the designing engineers as well as the bridge salesmen of those days. Conditions improved when owners began to prepare or have prepared their own definite plans and specifications, and contractors could bid more closely and intelligently.

Recalling the problem in iron bridge construction as that infant industry developed, Richard Humphrey[2] in 1907 appealed to the American Concrete Institute (at that time called National Association of Cement Users) to forestall similar tragedies in the then-burgeoning field of concrete construction. "The present condition of the art of concrete or reinforced concrete construction," he said, "is not unlike the condition of the iron business in its early history. . . . It will only be by determined action that the present abuses can be curbed and the fair name of concrete preserved. . . . Let each of us put our shoulder to the wheel, thereby controlling this rapid movement in the application of cement to constructive use, lest it get away from us and go on to destruction."

Concrete at that time was relatively new as a major construction material, and its increasing use had been accompanied by a concentration of failures, as is frequently the case with new materials. If these failures had been brought to light and their warnings properly heeded, repetition of troubles stemming from the same causes might have been more readily prevented. The *Engineering News*[5] made an effort in this direction in its 1903 editorial:

> "One of the special advantages usually claimed for concrete
> work is that it can be safely built by unskilled labor, but in
> view of some recent accidents which have occurred it appears
> well to point out that this principle is not of universal applica-
> tion. For concrete in large masses such as abutments, founda-
> tions, retaining walls, etc., there is no doubt that unskilled labor
> should be employed, under proper supervision. But for certain
> other classes of work, girders and floors in concrete buildings,

---

* A reviewer who summarized these cases noted that the first 251 collapses occurred in ten years, while the second 251 occurred in eight years. In the years 1888-1891 inclusive, there were 162 such accidents.

it appears that some degree of skilled labor should be employed, or at least the entire work should be under strict and constant supervision by skilled foremen, architects or engineers. In the carpentry work for forms and falsework especially, there is frequent evidence that the weight of the mass to be supported and the hydrostatic pressure of very wet concrete in columns are not realized by the men who are entrusted with the construction of this part of the work. When concrete has once thoroughly set it will stand very hard service and even overload or abuse, but it should be very strongly impressed upon the men engaged in concrete construction that the wet mass is simply a dead weight to be supported, having absolutely no supporting power in itself. If steel bars, rods, etc., are used, these simply add to the weight of the wet mass. The fall of a concrete floor at Chicago, noted in our issue of December 4, seems to have been due entirely to an ignorant man blindly following out instructions which were probably extremely indefinite. He was told to go in and knock out some of the shoring, and he proceeded to knock out every bent, until the unsupported concrete gave way, and its fall broke through other completed concrete work below.

"Another accident which is said to be due to failure of falsework is recorded elsewhere in this issue. In another case which came under our personal observation a laborer was found knocking away some of the struts and braces under a green concrete floor, simply because (as he told the superintendent when discovered) a carpenter told him to get some lumber. When informed that he stood a good chance of killing himself and other men in the work, as well as wrecking the building, he simply became surly and appeared to think that the superintendent was making a fuss about nothing. The same applies to the concreting gang. The men usually employed for this class of work simply dump the concrete into the forms without discretion, frequently being left without observation by even a foreman for a considerable time. This is especially serious at the junctions of concrete columns and girders. We have heard of instances where forms for girders were filled before the form at the junction with the column was complete, the men simply putting a piece of plank at the end of the form for the girder to make a stop-off and prevent the concrete from running out. If the column is built immediately and the block pulled out there may be little harm done, but there is the liability that the plank may be forgotten, or the concrete of the girder allowed to set before the concrete for the column is deposited. In either of these cases the girder becomes a cantilever, being partially or entirely separated from the column, instead of forming a homogeneous mass with it. There is no doubt that a great deal of concrete work is built by men who are really not competent to undertake it, and that much more work is done without sufficiently strict and continuous expert supervision to ensure the

best and safest results. In view of the enormous increase in the
use of concrete, and in the variety of purposes for which it is
used, it is well for engineers to bear these facts in mind."

This editorial should be required reading at least once a year for
everyone involved in concrete construction.

Early reinforced concrete construction also suffered from the same
problem that had plagued the iron bridge industry . . . competitive
bidding by engineer-contractors with no responsible professional engineer to safeguard the owner's interest. Construction was at times a
deal between the owner and the contractor only; in other cases, an
architect was engaged to prepare a "design" or general layout, but it
was quite common to have the structural parts and fireproofing designed by the bidders. The prospective contractors were doing the
engineering at no extra cost. As the *Engineering News* reported[6] in
1906, "It is extremely uncommon for a consulting engineer to be employed on reinforced concrete structures. It is considered a waste of
money, and by the prospective contractor an undesired reflection on
his ability and honesty."

In 1918, the American Railway Engineering Association published
a study of failures of concrete structures[1] with the subheading "A
Compilation of Failed Concrete Structures and Lessons to be Drawn
Therefrom." The study covers 25 years of failures and classifies the
causes under the headings:

1. Improper design
2. Poor materials or poor workmanship
3. Premature loading or removal of the forms before complete
   setting
4. Subsidence of foundations, fire, etc.

The final conclusion is: "The one thing which these failures conclusively point to is that all good concrete construction should be subjected to rigid inspection. It should be insisted upon that the inspector shall force the contractor to follow out the specifications to the
most minute details. He must see that the materials used are proper
and are properly mixed and deposited, also that the forms are sufficiently strong and that they are not removed until after the concrete
is set. It is believed that only by this kind of inspection is it possible
to guard against the failure of concrete structures." So the 1903 editorial advice still held in 1918; the lesson was not learned and still
has not been learned by some.

In 1924, Edward Godfrey, a structural engineering consultant
known for his frank and tireless criticism of improper design tech-

niques, published *Engineering Failures and Their Lessons*,[7] a book of discussions, articles, and letters on failures. Various phases of civil engineering are covered in the 20 chapters. The variety of references and scope of coverage indicate great effort to present a comprehensive picture. Included is a summary of concrete structures which failed between 1900 and 1920; among the 24 examples cited, he attributes most to frost, insufficient shear resistance, poor reinforcement of beam-column connections, "rodded" columns, and excessive sag. The discussion of concrete failures is somewhat colored by Godfrey's two fixed ideas regarding concrete design: (1) stirrups have no value in shear resistance; and (2) rodded columns* are inherently weak.

RECENT PUBLICATIONS

In recent years, many articles and a few books have appeared to warn of the dangers in concrete construction and to plead for open discussion and information of actual incidents. There seems to be less restriction to such open discussion in the fields of foundations, earth structures, and bridges than in the work generally classified as super-structures.

Lossier's *La Pathologie du Beton Arme*,[8] published in 1952, cites many examples of failures, mostly in concrete frames and special structures. Conclusions are similar to those of the 1918 AREA paper[1] plus warnings that errors in the choice of framing and in design details are most important factors in causing failures. A 1955 edition of this work was translated into English in 1962.

Engineering Structural Failures,[9] by Rolt Hammond (1956), covers the causes and results of failures in modern structures of various types. The foreword quotes some interesting remarks by Robert Stevenson, speaking as president of the Institution of Civil Engineers (England) in 1856. Summing up a paper, Stevenson said he hoped

> "that all the casualties and accidents, which had occurred during their progress would be noticed in revising the paper; for nothing was so instructive to the Younger Members of the Profession, as records of accidents in large works, and of the means, of repairing the damage. A faithful account of those accidents and the means by which the consequences were met, was really more valuable than a description of the most successful works. The older Engineers derived their most useful store of experience, from the observations of those casualties which had oc-

---

* He describes these as square or rectangular, reinforced with "slender upright rods [also in square or rectangular configuration] tied at intervals of a foot with a little rod or wire."

curred to their own works, and it was most important that they should be faithfully recorded in the archives of the Institution."

Hammond deals in a broad way with the spectacular collapses in the fields of earthworks, dams, maritime structures, buildings and bridges, underground structures, and welded structures, as well as with vibration problems. Although the work is of general interest, his over-all treatment of the subject does not permit instructive or usable recommendations in the field of reinforced concrete.

Professor Szechy of Budapest prepared a compilation of foundation failures, primarily European occurrences, which appeared in English translation in 1961.[10] This work includes a number of well-documented cases; errors are frankly described, and a careful analysis of the cause of each failure is made. Champion's *Failure and Repair of Concrete Structures*,[11] which was also published in 1961, has a brief section on the causes of failure, but is primarily a treatment of repair techniques for existing damaged or deteriorated structures.

Building Failures,[12] by Thomas McKaig (1962), reports in case study form on the important aspects of more than 200 major and minor structural failures. Examples are limited almost entirely to *buildings,* with much of the information drawn from *Engineering News-Record* and its predecessor publications, covering a period from 1895 to 1960. Some 30 cases are listed as reinforced concrete failures, and concrete problems figure in a number of the other failures described.

The 1962 Congress of the International Prestressed Concrete Federation in Rome included, for the first time, a number of contributions on the subject of failures in prestressed concrete pointing out the need for a new look at accepted procedures and details. A recent paper[13] summarizes many of the incidents reported in Rome and also describes some of the difficulties with prestressing in the United States.

Another recent (1963) work in German by Günter Mall[14] covers building failures in terms of the materials used, showing how their properties contribute to damage and malfunctioning of structures. This book is copiously illustrated with photographs of floors, roofs, walls, and foundations with cracks, spalls, pop-outs, bulges and other defects. Paint, plaster, masonry, and other materials as well as concrete are included.

The present monograph joins these latest treatments of the delicate but necessary record of failures, their causes, and how to avoid them. It has been prepared with hopeful concentration on the ancient admonition of Confucius:

"If you wish to control the future, study the past."

3

Design Deficiencies
Leading to Failure

THE TERM "FAILURE" indicates not only structural collapse, but a wide range of nonconformity with design expectations or requirements—such as unwanted settlements, deformations, cracks, bulges, and misalignments. Although failure is frequently attributed to a coincidence of factors rather than just a single cause, cases selected for this chapter are those where design errors or inadequacies were major factors in the chain of events leading to failure. Insofar as direct mistakes in calculations are concerned, design errors leading to failure are relatively rare, although a few failures and near-failures of this sort are described later. Errors in the assumptions regarding loading and flexural conditions are more common, along with poor or poorly supervised detailing and drafting; careless treatment of connections between members; improper location and spacing of reinforcing bars and splices; inadequate attention to thermal and shrinkage effects; and insufficient consideration of secondary stresses.

Reinforced concrete design is based on simplifying assumptions which do not correlate perfectly with actual conditions in the structure. For example, arbitrary assumption of the location of points of inflection, a procedure quite popular up to 25 years ago when the free support moments were split as desired into positive and negative factors, often resulted in cracks since the structure refused to accept an assumption which was not in compliance with actual relative stiffnesses of the contiguous members.

Designers may not realize to what extent actual experience has formed the basis for safe design, and that design practice is subject to continuing modification as more and more structures are observed. The knowledge gleaned from failures is one important source from which changes in design practice have come. Some of the spectacular collapses of past decades have also led to the establishment and modification of building codes.

Meeting building code requirements, however, does not guarantee the success of a structure; the designer must exercise wider judgment and responsibility. A designer sometimes acts in good faith, working within code limits on accepted design practices of his day, and yet he produces a design that proves unsatisfactory or even dangerous. He overlooks the fact that most reinforced concrete codes contain only *minimum* requirements, and often do not clearly indicate the limits of their applicability. Provisions which will give safe designs for ordinary members may be quite unsafe to use for large and complicated ones.

Failures are more likely to occur with a new, relatively untried material—such as reinforced concrete was sixty years ago—or with new structural uses of any construction materials, where design assumptions have not stood the test of time. Radical new design procedures or new materials should not be accepted without a critical, even pessimistic, analysis of whether the promised saving of material or some other benefit will justify any accompanying reduction in the safety factor or in the surplus computed strengths to cover contingencies in unknown loadings and in material compliances.

"Transplanting" designs from one site to another, or quick redesign of standardized plans, may also lead to failures. Careful checking of these adapted designs is necessary. Thorough checking for errors at every stage—design, detailing, drafting—is a costly but important part of all good practice. Coordination of mechanical, electrical, heating, and plumbing plans with the structural design is also necessary to avoid concentrations of openings or voids that will weaken structural members (see flat plate failure, p. 30, where holes prevented continuity of slab reinforcement).

Dangerous errors may be introduced when a design is hastily altered before or during construction; changes from the original design figured in the viaduct collapse below and numerous other cases described later. Contracts for engineering services should require all plan changes to be approved by the original designer.

EARLY INCIDENTS

In an era before the adoption of building codes, and before the requirement of engineering registration, a little knowledge could indeed be a dangerous thing. A review of early failures in reinforced concrete construction—even incidents extending into the 1920's—reveals so many things wrong on some of these jobs that one could pick the "cause" of failure according to his personal bias. For example, since many collapses took place when supporting formwork was removed, it was easy to ascribe failure to premature removal of forms.*

Structural design was seldom found wanting. Protesting this unwillingness to acknowledge design errors, Edward Godfrey† listed a number of early failures which he ascribed to design deficiencies, and the previously cited AREA *Bulletin*[1] also carried a number of collapses attributed to inadequate design. Only three cases will be described; the compounding of bad practices both in design and construction is evident in these examples, but it is believed defective design was a major factor in each case.

VIADUCT AT PARIS EXPOSITION—1900[1, 15, 16]

A reinforced concrete viaduct was built by the Celestial Globe Company in 1900 over the Avenue Suffern in Paris so that visitors to the Paris Exposition could attend the exhibit without leaving the enclosure of the exposition grounds. The bridge was 375 ft long, 16½ ft wide, and some 15 ft above the street. It consisted of 30-ft spans supported on 12-in. square concrete columns. The deck was 6-in. concrete, reinforced two ways and supported on light steel beams resting on the piers. Longitudinal stressed cables bounded the walkway as railings. The concrete was 1 week old when workmen started to remove the centering. This work was halted when a slight sinking was observed, but police failed to stop traffic beneath the bridge. Following sounds of cracking, the section where shoring had been removed collapsed and dragged the rest after it.

It is reported that no detailed plans of the bridge were made, simply a sketch to see how much iron should be ordered. The contractor arranged with the surveyor to make two angles in the bridge instead of laying it out straight, in order to save some trees which were in the way. Evidence

---

* Godfrey remarks (Reference 7, p. 106) that "it is on record that interested persons attributed a failure in August to removal of column forms in ten days, and set up the claim of cold weather; also an interested person argued publicly that the reason the Bell St. Warehouse test was a failure was because concrete 116 days old was not seasoned."

† Reference 7, pp. 107-118.

was conflicting as to whether the piers were increased in size to take the greater thrust caused by the change. The resulting oblique forces practically kicked the deck off the piers, and when the bridge fell a number of people were trapped underneath. It is believed that pillars and columns were too weak, and that vibration from vehicles below precipitated the collapse. Concrete at the collapse site appaeared damp and crumbly. The court and experts who investigated pronounced the consulting engineer and the contractors "guilty of the most culpable negligence."

BIXBY HOTEL, LONG BEACH, CALIFORNIA—1906[17]

The hotel comprised five stories plus basement in an H-shaped plan as shown in Figure 3.1. It was originally designed with twisted-bar reinforced slabs, but the owner decided to change most of the slab construction to a hollow tile system common at the time. Floors were designed for 150 psf live load on the first floor and 60 psf live load on other floors. Columns were 21 in. square at the basement level, round and tapered from 22 to 26 in. on the first floor, 12 and 16 in. square on the second floor, decreasing to 8 in. square on fourth and fifth floors. The specified reinforcement was the same for all these columns—four round ½-in. bars. Evidence gleaned later from the wreckage indicated that some columns had wire ties spaced about 16 in. apart, and some had no ties (as built). Columns were about

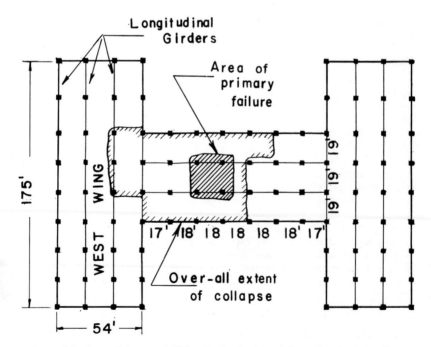

Figure 3.1—General layout of Bixby Hotel, showing girder and column locations and areas of collapse. Note absence of transverse girders for slab support.

18 ft on centers in both directions, as shown in Figure 3.1, and there were longitudinal girders between columns, but no transverse girders supporting the slab.

Concreting of the fifth floor had been completed about October 22, and work on the roof began October 29. The roof slab was 4 in. thick, with 8x8-in. beams spaced 8 ft apart. Reinforcement was wire fabric and ½-in. rods. Concreting was still in progress on the roof November 9, 1906, when a large section of the center wing collapsed all the way to the base-ment, killing ten of the numerous workmen busy on various floors of the building. Exact location of the initial failure was difficult to establish; the contractor and superintendent who were on the roof at the time said the roof seemed to sink suddenly about 12 ft without any perceptible sound of impact. A worker on the third floor said the floor sagged under his feet at the same time that debris fell from above. Since concrete appeared to be of satisfactory quality, and there was no settlement of footings, early re-ports[17] attributed collapse to weakness in either the finished permanent columns or the shoring supporting the roof, or both of these factors.

Shoring between the fifth floor and the roof forms was 2x4's and 4x4's, sway braced on alternate rows, wedged up directly from the floor without bearing plank. Some of the shores were spliced at midheight.[18] Some shoring remained in place between fourth and fifth floors. The in-vestigating coroner's jury established no criminal liability, but attributed the collapse to "prematurely removing part of the timbers supporting the fifth floor, and proceeding with construction of the roof before the cement beneath was properly cured." A quick check of the weight of roof alone shows it almost equaled the design live load of 60 psf on the fifth floor, without allowing for formwork or construction loads. The fifth floor thus could have been overloaded even if it had attained full design strength; shoring or reshoring was clearly required for its support.

The collapse aroused attention of the engineering profession, and their numerous remarks in the engineering press at the time seem to substantiate the charge that serious defects existed in the design. Columns were said to be underdesigned, shear reinforcement was lacking in the girders (girders showed diagonal shear cracks under dead load alone),[19] and there were no haunches, brackets or reinforcement to provide rigidity at beam-column connections. Well documented statements indicated column stresses as much as three times the recommended allowable at that time.

COWHEY GARAGE, DETROIT, MICHIGAN—1912

A collapse occurred on November 15, 1912, in a three-story and base-ment garage structure in Detroit, while concreting was in progress on the third floor.[20] The building was 120 ft deep, 66½ ft wide at the rear and 70 ft at the front, of beam-and-column construction, with brick curtain walls and a tile-and-concrete slab. The 6x12x12-in. tiles, which had a 2-in. cover of concrete and 4-in. reinforced joists between tiles, spanned something less than 17 ft between the T-beams.

Concrete work on the second floor was finished October 15. Work had proceeded so that concrete was being placed on the third floor at the rear of the building November 15 when, after brief warning by cracking supports and sagging girders, the month-old second floor collapsed, killing three men and injuring a number of others. Figure 3.2 indicates the area of collapse. No columns failed, but beams in the collapsed area pulled out of their supporting columns. There was no evidence of reinforcement connection between these members except for an inch or two intrusion of the beam rods into the columns; these pulled out leaving holes in the columns.

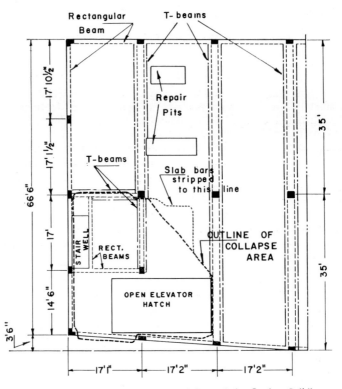

Figure 3.2—Plan of part of the second floor of the Cowhey Building showing framing and area of collapse. Openings for stairs and elevator, plus incomplete framing around elevator hatch, contributed to general weakness in the failed area.

At the time of failure, the third floor was supported on shores which had been removed from beneath the second floor, leaving only occasional posts of uncertain strength there.

The concrete trade press of the day called it "another workmanship failure,"[21] but the coroner's jury brought a verdict of negligence against both the designer and the contractor. The *Engineering News* pointed out a combination of bad practices responsible for the accident: poor quality concrete, weaknesses in design, and lack of proper supervision at all stages of the job. The architect's drawings were turned over to a steel supplier who prepared the structural design. The contractor, hired under an unusual agreement,* did little more than furnish equipment for the job. General supervision was in the hands of a hired superintendent, who resigned before the job was finished, leaving supervision to the hoisting engineer on the job. Plans were approved by the Detroit building department, but apparently this was only a formality as the department allegedly had no one competent in reinforced concrete design to do checking. Apparently no one other than the owner had any continuing authority or responsibility for the job.

Beams in the failed area were stressed to a probable 1500 psi compression in the concrete; code design values at the time permitted 650 psi. Note the openings for stairs and elevator in the failed area, with incomplete framing around the elevator hatch. A construction hoist was placed in this hatch, connected to concrete forms at the third floor level, and no doubt added shock and vibration to other loads on the new structure.

CALCULATION ERRORS

With growing experience in all types of reinforced concrete structures and the establishment of various controls through which a job passes, the possibility of a gross error in design actually getting to the construction stage is increasingly remote. However, concrete designs need more than a numerical checking; a cursory examination of design drawings by an experienced engineer or builder will often show up flaws in design. The near-failure cases which follow show how some errors were detected, forestalling costly collapse.

One design error was caught just before placing concrete in the forms of 65-ft roof beams spanning a school auditorium in Yonkers, N.Y., in 1925. About 4 sq. in. of reinforcement had been called for and placed, but the design should have required 40 sq in. At that time, girders of this size were most unusual, and the error was picked up by a young engineer on the contractor's staff. These girders would have undoubtedly failed if the error had not been corrected.

Rogers[22] reported a similar case with the reinforced concrete slab and beam roof system for a new public school gymnasium. The beams spanned 54 ft, framing into deep, narrow spandrels. Although the structure was designed by a reputable engineer, there was an error in the calculations, and less than one-third of the necessary reinforcement was provided. The mistake was discovered after the concrete was cast, but while the formwork was still in place. An additional system of partial prestressing was added to compensate for the design error.

---

* Reportedly there was an additional bonus to the contractor of all the building materials left after completion!

More recently another design error was found just in time in Birmingham, Ala. Omission of a major hanger load suspended from the main girders of the added third deck in a football stadium was not picked up until an inquisitive engineer employed by the steel erector questioned why all the girders were identical, even though only the middle section had a mezzanine. The design engineer immediately recognized the mistake, ordered use of the stand cancelled, and rapidly arranged for the welding of additional angles to the chords of the plate girders.

SHEAR RESISTANCE

In spite of extensive research programs and in spite of the successful use of concrete in structures of all types, it is still true that the fundamental behavior of concrete members in transferring shear load is not fully understood. This is no doubt the reason that in certain cases design practices that have been used have resulted in costly failures. Insufficient shear resistance may produce a failure without warning, and at least a local collapse results. Often this triggers collapse of a greater area or of a complete structure.

The complex problems of determining shear capacity of reinforced concrete members are not readily soluble either by theory or testing. Permissible shearing stresses have been derived from data obtained in laboratory tests of units which may not entirely simulate either the loading conditions or the structural system occurring in many buildings. The recommended design procedures to provide shear resistance have undergone considerable change in the various codes, and differ considerably today in countries where modern construction is a large industry.

Though strict dependence on code provisions has resulted in an overwhelming number of properly functioning structures, it is always necessary to make sure that the structure under design conforms to conditions forming the basis of code requirements before these minimum regulations are used as the sole design criteria. Warnings from investigators, as have occurred on the shear design problem, often remain academic and controversial until difficulties are observed in actual construction. Such a difficulty—the much publicized, discussed, and investigated rigid frame warehouse failures described below—intensified doubts and questions about shear calculation provisions of "Building Code Requirements for Reinforced Concrete (ACI 318-51)," and led to revisions in the updated code (ACI 318-56).

Because of the suddenness of shear failure, the basic design philosophy of the latest revised code, ACI 318-63, is to assure that shear will not govern in ultimate strength design. In other words, a shear failure should not occur, even in a heavily overloaded member, before the full flexural strength and toughness of the member have been developed. Working stress design procedures in 318-63 were developed essentially by using a factor of two in scaling down ultimate strength design procedures.

AIR MATERIEL COMMAND (AMC) WAREHOUSE, SHELBY, OHIO—1955[*]

About 4000 sq ft of the roof of a recently built one-story warehouse at Wilkins Air Force Depot fell suddenly Aug. 17, 1955, when rigid frame supports collapsed. The roof carried no loads other than its own weight at the time, but there is evidence to suggest significant axial loading in the framing due to temperature and shrinkage effects (see p. 43).

The warehouse was a six-span rigid frame building, 400 ft wide and 2000 ft long. Building frame and roof covering were separated by an over-lapped continuous longitudinal expansion joint near the center of the 400-ft width, and by double frames spaced at 200-ft intervals along the 2000-ft length, yielding bays like the one shown in Figure 3.3 where collapse occurred. The six spans were formed of haunched rigid frames with each span about 67 ft; frames were approximately 33 ft on centers.

Frames of the warehouse at Wilkins Air Force Depot were built in accordance with a design dated April, 1952, reinforced as shown in Figure 3.3. As a result of experience during construction, the 1952 design was revised in March 1954 to provide top bars and nominal stirrups (.06 percent) for the full length of the frames. Several warehouses similar to that at Wilkins were constructed at other locations in accordance with the 1954 revised design.[†]

Each frame girder, 400 ft long, was concreted in a single placement during one working day. Vertical steel plate construction joints were set at the center of each span before concrete was placed. However, placement was along the beam and past the plate in a continuous operation, and the effectiveness of these joints in limiting shrinkage stresses is doubtful.

---

[*] A similar warehouse roof collapse occurred at Robins Air Force Base near Macon, Ga., in the fall of 1956. Supporting frames were the same shape as used at Wilkins, but the top steel was continuous and nominal stirrups had been provided. Here widening cracks in the rigid frames were observed in August, with one crack becoming ½ in. on September 4. Some 6000 sq ft of the roof, including two adjacent girders of the longer arm at an expansion joint, failed at 3:05 A.M. Sept. 5, 1956. This area was in a 400x1600-ft warehouse which had been in use for 18 months. A building of similar design at the same base, 400x400 ft, which was constructed as a separate contract with a very slow progress schedule, showed practically no cracking. (It seems that the extent of shrinkage and resulting axial tensions may be somewhat related to the speed of concreting or to the extent of each separate placement.)

[†] The AMC warehouse, near Macon, Ga., which failed in 1956, was built according to this revised design.

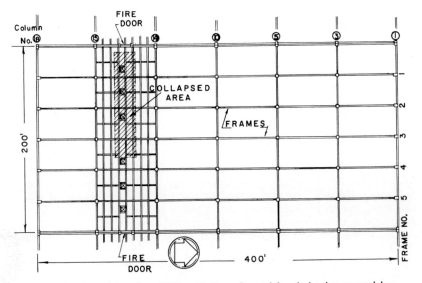

Figure 3.3—Plan of Bay 6 at Wilkins Air Force Depot (above) showing general lay-out and extent of failure. Drawing below shows elevation of bent span that col-lapsed, indicating position of reinforcement according to 1952 (original) design.

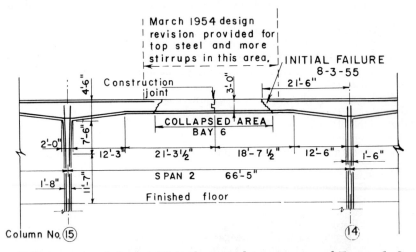

Collapse occurred August 17 in the second interior span of Frames 1, 2, and 3 (Figure 3.3). Severe cracking had been observed August 3 in Frame 1 (which had been concreted Feb. 10, 1954), and the girder was supported at that time on temporary shoring. (Note that the cracks appeared in warm weather almost a year after full dead load had been applied.) However, it failed when the adjacent bays collapsed on the 17th, leaving a collapsed area as shown in Figure 3.3. The frame failure was about 1½ ft beyond the cut-off of straight top negative reinforcement downward through the cut-off of some of the straight bottom reinforcement. Original design calculations indicated that a small positive moment existed at the point of failure under all loading conditions.

Structural design had been carried out in accord with minimum requirements of generally accepted and commonly used American building codes. Materials and workmanship were shown to be in accord with specifications and common practice. Concrete strengths as determined by core tests exceeded the minimum required. All major items seemed to be up to standard in terms of prevailing practices of the day; yet failure occurred.

It is believed that failure took place by a combination of diagonal tension (shear) due to dead load and axial tension due to shrinkage and temperature change. Circumstantial evidence suggested that high friction forces were developed in the expansion joint consisting of one steel plate sliding on another; some plates showed no indication of relative displacement since their installation.

Contrary to the common experience with failures, these events have been thoroughly reported and exhaustively studied. Since so much of this information is readily available[23-27] only the major lessons are summarized here:

1. Codes are often accepted without question by many designers as affording total judgment on the subject. It must be remembered that a code provides minimum requirements and governs only as far as it is applicable.

2. Direct tensile stress due to shrinkage, temperature, ineffective expansion joints, or other causes added to the tension caused by gravity loads can be very serious, especially at points of inflection.

3. Straight top bars and straight bottom bars to resist negative and positive moments are not as effective as bent bars in preventing total collapse or resisting diagonal web stresses.

4. Straight bars should not be cut off exactly according to the moment-envelope curves but should run on past the theoretical cut-off for development.

5. Even a small amount of web reinforcement prevents sudden failure by diagonal tension.

6. Sliding type steel-on-steel expansion joints are not effective. Open slots an inch or so wide are much more effective.

As already noted, this failure led to changes in shear provisions of the ACI Building Code. It also led to new plans for warehouse structures; all construction on new warehouses of this type was halted immediately following the failure. A revised design was developed and plans were made to strengthen existing structures of the same

Figure 3.4—External "stirrups" of steel strapping were used to strengthen existing AMC Warehouse frames built according to the ill-fated 1952 design. Note steel angle at lower corner of girder. Photograph was taken during repair operations at Robins Air Force Base.

design by the addition of external stirrups of tensioned steel strapping with steel angles at the lower corners of the girders (Figure 3.4). It was found necessary to tap straps manually during the tightening operation so that unit stress in all four legs of the band would be fairly uniform. Cost of the repair procedure plus the cost of temporary shoring of cracked girders, labor of moving and replacing stored goods, and final cleanup was only a small percentage of the value of the warehouses, although it totaled millions of dollars.

LIFT SLAB WAREHOUSE ROOF, OJUS, FLORIDA—1952

Another shear failure occurred during load testing of a rather unusual lift slab structure[28] at Ojus, Fla., May 9, 1952. The one-story, 14 ft high warehouse was roofed with eight waffle-type slabs. Each slab was 50 ft square, supported on four columns 30 ft apart, leaving a 10-ft cantilever around the edge of each slab unit. The slab was built of precast dome pan units, 2 ft square, 13 in. deep, with 2-in. lips at the bottom to form the bottom of cast-in-place concrete joists (Figure 3.5). The precast waffle forms were omitted at the columns to leave a solid slab cap about 4 ft square, and 13 in. deep. Columns, 10 inches in diameter, were cast in place, and provided with a metal pipe collar for attaching the lift slab.

There was no prestressing, and apparently standard design methods were followed.

After two earlier failures (March 18 and April 2)[29, 30] which were attributed to erection problems, authorities ordered a load test before the building was occupied. One roof slab unit flooded with 8¾ in. of water, equivalent to full live load, met deflection and recovery requirements satisfactorily. A second unit, being tested to 50 percent overload, collapsed when the water depth reached 12½ in.[31]

The specialist who investigated[32] the incident attributed failure to excessive shear on a section without stirrups. The top steel over the columns overlapped the bottom steel by not more than 2 ft, and there were no bent bars or stirrups to reinforce a diagonal shear surface. The line of failure from the end of the short straight top bar to the end of short straight bottom bar *crossed no reinforcement*. Further, the bond between smooth walls of the precast dome pans and the cast-in-place concrete of the joist was of doubtful value in permitting the precast units to contribute to shear resistance. The dome units themselves cracked as shown in Figure 3.5. As a corrective measure, U-bolt yokes were placed around the joists to increase the horizontal shear strength.

This failure brings out several points for designers to keep in mind:

1. Unusual designs such as this one require special attention to the details of connection, plus careful consideration of bond that assures composite action of the precast and cast-in-place slab components.

2. Straight top bars and straight bottom bars cut short around negative and positive moment curves do not provide reinforcement for diagonal tension. Allowable ultimate diagonal tension in unreinforced concrete at such joints may be small, making reinforcement desirable.

3. It must be remembered that points of inflection and moment-

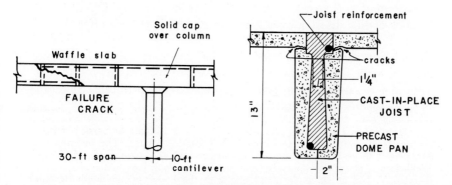

Figure 3.5—Sketch shows how precast dome pans formed a waffle slab with cast-in-place joist between adjacent domes. Detail indicates solid cap at column, and location of failure crack with respect to supporting column.

envelope curves are not stationary but move with different load patterns, settlement of supports, shrinkage of concrete, and temperature changes.

At first glance, the tragic failure[33-36] described below resembled a formwork collapse. However, it probably resulted from excessive punching shear in the flat plates at the columns.

FLAT PLATE OFFICE BUILDING, JACKSON, MICHIGAN—1956

The building was approximately cross-shaped, measuring a maximum of 254x217 ft. Reinforced concrete flat plate floors (no column capitals or drop panels) were 10 in. thick, supported on square columns spaced 24 ft on centers in both directions. Columns rested on concrete-filled pipe piles driven to bedrock. Typical columns were 25 in. square at the basement level, 23 in. square between first and second floors, and 20 in. square between the second and fourth floors.

First and second floors were several weeks old at the time of the accident, and forms and shores had been removed. The third floor concrete was at least 20 days old; forms had been removed, and the slab was re-shored to the second floor, and was carrying the formwork for the fourth floor. Concrete had been placed in the fourth floor forms only a short while on October 3 when most of the east wing, an area about 72x144 ft, dropped all the way to the cellar. The other three wings were little damaged except where they adjoined the collapsed section.

Significantly almost all of the columns remained standing full height after the collapse (Figure 3.6). Top-story column forms remained in place and very little reinforcement projected from the free-standing columns at any floor level. Plans indicated 10x14-in. duct openings in the slab along two adjacent faces of some interior columns, which of course prevented slab steel from running through the columns. The design called for a square "spider"* around each interior column within the slab thickness, but how these assemblies could be placed within the zone of high shear and still permit the duct openings is not clear.

According to *Concrete Construction*[36] at least seven different investigations of this disaster were contemplated a short time after the collapse; lucid explanations and conclusions were never published. A special commission appointed by the governor of Michigan was charged with the responsibility to "evaluate the reasons for the disaster and to make appropriate recommendations for the prevention of future tragedies of this kind."

---

* Described in *Engineering News-Record*[33] as having square tie bars placed concentrically in horizontal planes around each interior column. The innermost tie bar, placed 4½ in. below the top of the slab, was 42 in. square, made of #5 rod. Welded to it at regular intervals were eight 12-in. long bars in the shape of an inverted V, laid at an angle of 45 deg with the horizontal and with the apex pointed upward, and toward the column. Two other tie bars, placed 3 in. below the top of the slab, were made of #3 bars, 56 in. and 73 in. square, respectively. They had 12 and 16, respectively, of the V-bars welded to them.

Figure 3.6—Columns remained standing following collapse of flat plate floors in this Jackson, Michigan, structure. Probable failure cause was excessive punching shear in the flat plates where reinforcement continuity was interrupted at some of the columns.

Late in 1957, more than a year after the accident, the commission finally issued its official report which stated that it

> "attributes the collapse of the building to 'human failure.' From a technical standpoint, no single factor can be pinpointed as the proximate cause of failure. The committee questions various aspects of the design, construction, and supervision of this building project and the owner's participation therein."

Unfortunately the committee did not elaborate on the nature of the "human failure" responsible for the collapse, or explain which aspects of "design, construction, and supervision" it found questionable.

Calling this report "so vague in its findings as to be virtually useless," *Engineering News-Record* charged that "the committee failed to discharge its duties both to the public and to the engineering profession. It has also been unfair to the designers and the contractor by issuing broad accusations to which they cannot reply without knowledge of the specifics."

In spite of a disappointing official report, a valuable lesson is dramatized by this failure:

> The lack of load transfer from slab to column indicates the advisability of renewing the older concept of punching shear investigation as part of any plate design. Equally important, in these

Figure 3.7—Punching shear failure of lightweight flat plate occurred at this column when the slab was overloaded by shoring of floor above before reaching adequate strength.

days of air conditioned buildings where the concrete frame becomes merely an enclosure of the mechanical equipment, is the close coordination of structural requirements with the holes, sleeves, and loads required by the mechanical designs. Flat plate floors are feasible and economical only if uninterrupted continuity at columns is provided. No one would agree to a design for a plate footing with openings at the face of the columns. The structural requirements for a flat slab or plate floor are the same as for a footing.*

Inadequate shear resistance was blamed again when a plaza deck at the Imperial House on East 69th Street in New York collapsed as several columns punched through the lightweight concrete flat plate. There was a small overload when the drain clogged and 3 ft of soil became fully saturated. Reinforcing bars appeared not to adhere to the concrete at the columns, and a small column cap planned by the designer had been omitted. A similar design for another plaza showed no failure where the soil remained dry.

BEARING SUPPORT PROBLEMS

Otherwise well-designed concrete and steel structures have failed because of poorly designed bearing supports and connections to those supports. Static design of roof slabs often indicates that very light

* Suggestions of interest to designers were presented in an article by Stephen D. Teetor, "Pitfalls in Flat-Plate Construction—and How to Avoid Them," in *Engineering News-Record*, V. 152, No. 11, Mar. 18, 1954, pp. 49–50, 52.

posts are sufficient. However, if loading is unbalanced, or if something is leaned against a post (such as the stacking of lumber or masonry units during construction), corkscrew rotation is possible without any change in dimension of the roof or of the posts, and failure results. This happened to several isolated roof shelters in a New York state hospital; each was a 20 ft square concrete deck on a square of steel channels, with four pipe columns. Rigid knee connections were added after the rotation had been stopped by timber bracing.

Figure 3.8—Another case of punching shear in a flat plate where an opening in the slab adjacent to the column interrupted continuity of reinforcement.

Although the exact cause of the following failure was not reported,[37] job conditions suggest possible bearing problems.

FOLDED PLATE WAREHOUSE ROOF, SKOKIE, ILLINOIS—1959

Pretensioned slabs, 3 in. thick, supported on reinforced concrete bents, formed a folded plate roof for the combined office and warehouse (Figure 3.9). Over-all depth of the roof folds was 4½ ft, the peak-to-peak spacing was 10½ ft, and sides of the folded units sloped at about 45 degrees. A 52-ft width of adjoining 60-ft and 90-ft spans collapsed in February, 1959, while construction was still in progress on the building. The two collapsed spans were separate units with some negative reinforcement where they joined at the interior supporting bent.

Inner ends of nine of the ten 60-ft span slabs fell, with their outer ends leaning against the exterior three-column bent, but with anchorages torn loose. The entire tenth slab fell to the ground. Outer ends of the 90-ft span slabs (supported on common bent with the 60-ft spans) dropped to the ground with the other end remaining on the supports. It seems possible that the nonsymmetry of span with limited negative moment resistance at

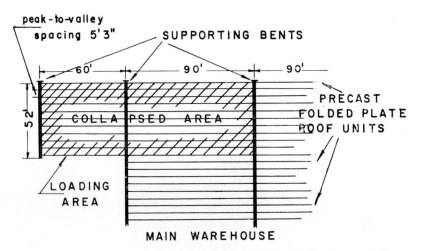

peak-to-valley
spacing 5'3"   SUPPORTING BENTS

MAIN WAREHOUSE

Figure 3.9—Sketch shows the warehouse layout at Skokie, Illinois, where part of a folded plate roof composed of precast, prestressed units collapsed.

the middle support, and scant bearing when the shoring was removed, resulted in a shift of position and failure. The greater part of the warehouse, covered by similar precast units on two 90-ft symmetrical spans showed no distress.

Two different investigating teams arrived at contradictory conclusions as to the cause of the following failure, but one main point at issue concerned design of the bearing detail at the beam-column connections, and it seems appropriate to describe it under bearing support problems.

WALKER FACTORY, HARRISONBURG, VIRGINIA—1960[38]

Five deaths added to gravity of material losses when 24,000 sq ft of a one-story factory building collapsed in November, 1960, near Harrisonburg, Va. Workers had just started erection of a new bay adjacent to the 24,000 sq ft area when the accident occurred. Precast columns were mounted over anchor bolts set in 6 ft square spread footings. Leveling and locking nuts were used to tie the columns' steel base plates to the footings. The 18 ft high columns for the building were of reinforced concrete 12 in. square, erected to form 40x50-ft bays. Prestressed concrete I-beams, 34 in. deep, spanned the 40 ft across the ends of each bay, and double-T sections, 6 ft wide and 15½ in. deep, spanned the 50 ft between beams to form the roof deck.

Erection welds specified between angles set in the column tops and angles cast in the ends of the beams had been made. Welders were working on connections between projecting bars at the top of the beams at the time of collapse. Beam-column bearing was specified at a minimum of 1½ in. and a maximum of 2 in. Column steel extended up between the beam ends (Figure 3.10), with the intention that the entire joint would be grouted and develop into a rigid type of connection. This final connection had not been completed at the time of collapse.

Two teams of expert investigators, one engaged by the fabricator-erector and one engaged by the architect, made detailed reports on this failure, bringing to light much significant information, even though they failed to concur on the "cause" of the accident. Investigators retained by the erector reported first, attributing the collapse to bearing failure at the beam-column connections. Some of their findings were:[39]

1. "A bearing failure could have occurred at any beam-to-column connection . . . at any time after the column had received full erection load." (They calculated a uniform bearing stress of 3460 psi at the bearing seat under dead load, and cited an ACI 318-56 building code provision for 1250 psi allowable bearing stress for edge loads on 5000-psi concrete.)

2. "Failure was imminent, and any slight shift brought about by temperature change, wind, movements resulting from erection activi-

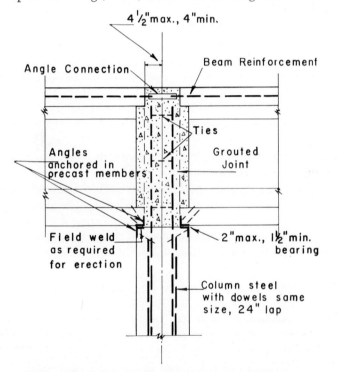

Figure 3.10—Typical interior beam-column connection as designed for the factory at Harrisonburg, Virginia, showing proposed grouted joint. Only the field welds at the base of the beam had been completed at the time of failure. Drawing from Engineering News-Record, December 15, 1960 (McGraw-Hill, Inc.).

ties or slight footing settlement could have produced the collapse . . .
The manner in which the failure was triggered is believed to be
immaterial."

3. "Close examination of columns in the collapsed portion of the
building confirmed the fact that bearing failures did occur."

Following the collapse, building erection was resumed and completed
with 14x14-in. columns and redetailed bearing seats. About eight months
later, investigators for the architect published their report, attributing the
collapse to "deficient lateral stability of the structure" because of faulty
erection procedures. The report cited five contributing factors:[40]

1. No temporary lateral bracing

2. Improper seating of columns on the footing

3. Inadequate welding at the beam-column connections

4. Forcing columns and beams laterally after erection against unbraced structure. (Reportedly two columns in the bay under construction when collapse occurred were 1½ to 2 in. out of plumb and
were pulled into line by a "come-along" attached to a column base
in the previously erected bay.)

5. Poor accessibility for field welding of beam-column connections.
Poor quality of welding and overloading of the erected structure by
stacking double-T's were also charged. Although job specifications
did not cover details of the welding procedure, the report held that
American Welding Society requirements should have been followed.

The architect's investigators also contended that the temporary bearing
between steel angles cast in the beams and columns could be designed for
higher allowable bearing stress recommended for post-tensioning anchorages.

Despite their divergent findings, these investigations served the constructive purpose of focusing much-needed attention on beam-column
connection design for prestressed structures. They also underscore the
value of having the designer write detailed specifications, approve
shop drawings, and inspect and approve fabricating and erecting procedures. The entire incident emphasizes the vigilant attention required of the contractor to insure safety of precast structures during
erection.

That concrete is a rigid material and therefore will transfer moments into supporting walls when the beams or slabs are embedded
should be a recognized fact. Yet bearing walls frequently are not
designed to resist these support moments and failures result. The
failure of a building under load test at Trenton, N.J., in 1903 is one
example; the Orlando, Florida, case is a more recent incident.

BRASS FACTORY, TRENTON, NEW JERSEY—1903[41]

The four-story 300x50-ft structure had reinforced concrete floors resting on exterior brick walls and on a center concrete girder supported on
columns. The 4½-in. slab spanning about 7 ft between 20 in. deep concrete

beams on 24-ft span was designed to compete with the then-normal timber floor mill building. The beams were embedded 12 in. in the supporting brick wall at the third floor level where failure originated.

The second floor had successfully stood under a load of 500 psf over a 30x30-ft area; bearing walls were 20 in. thick. A load of 150 tons had been placed December 7 on a 40x16-ft section of the third floor, and remained in place overnight. On the 8th, the remainder of the test load (all but 10 bags of sand) was put on, loading the floor to approximately double the 250-psf design load. Suddenly the concrete began to crack, the third-floor beams deflected, buckled the brick wall (16 in. thick at this level), and pulled out of their supports. The 12-in. bearing was insufficient to lock the beams and prevent rotation deflection, and of course the "fire cuts" that were common on the ends of embedded wood beams were not present to allow freedom of rotation. When the floor fell it wrecked the second floor below and killed two men at the first-floor level. Construction was by a reputable contractor, and investigation showed good concrete with no failure in the columns or footings. The walls were pierced by windows covering almost half the length. The fact that the test load of more than 500 psf and the collapsed third and second floors were stopped by the first floor speaks well of the quality of the concrete workmanship.

BLANKNER ELEMENTARY SCHOOL, ORLANDO, FLORIDA—1956[42]

A 32 ft wide section of a 56-ft span prestressed concrete roof over the cafeteria of the Frances L. Blankner Elementary School in Orlando, Fla., collapsed August 30, 1956, one week after its completion. The concrete masonry bearing wall toppled outward, and eight of the 5-ton pretensioned double-T slabs fell to the floor during a rainstorm at night (there were no witnesses or occupants). Shorter span roof members of similar design and construction were not affected. Although allegedly defective design of double-T roof members figured in this collapse, there was also insufficient bearing wall resistance. Walls were of 8-in. block, 14 ft high, without pilasters. There were three 7 ft wide window openings in the 32 ft of wall that collapsed.

A report[43] issued by the Prestressed Concrete Institute's investigating committee in 1957, included the following points:

1. Roof slab design was defective in that extreme fiber stresses exceeded the allowable.*
2. Cracking of the slab resulted in excessive deflection and the ponding of water on the roof; this caused further deflection and also rotation of the slab at the supports.
3. Bearing points of the slab on the concrete block wall were eccentric; rotation of the slabs had shifted the bearing point, causing collapse of the inadequately designed wall.

The committee expressed the belief[43] that this collapse would have been

---

* Some interesting engineering opinions on how the slab design might have permitted overstress when used on a 56-ft span were expressed in *Engineering News-Record*, July 11, 1957, p. 28. Initial overstress presumably led to cracking, increased deflections, and ponding of more than normal load of rainwater.

avoided if reinforced concrete pilasters and continuous concrete tie beam had been provided in the concrete block walls.

A failure quite similar to that at the Blankner School occurred in 1958 in Waltham, Mass., during erection of a one-story commercial building. The precast hollow slab roof fell and brought the top of the hollow block wall down with it. This roof was made of 30-ft hollow units, 9 in. thick by 16 in. wide, resting on an 8-in. hollow block wall, which like the one in Orlando was pierced by window openings.

DEFORMATION, SECONDARY STRESSES, AND ELASTIC CRACKING

Rigid connections of structural members introduce secondary stresses not normally computed. Under the general heading of secondary stresses are those cases where direct stress computations from normal loading would indicate no reason for cracking, but the resulting deformations induce stresses along other axes which may give trouble. Such conditions always exist, but stress intensity in the usual design is not high enough to overcome disregarded internal strengths such as the tensile value of concrete.

Structures like flat slabs transmit loading to supports in the easiest way but this may not be the pattern assumed by the design. Cracks then result as the frame becomes hinged and tries to conform to the assumed pattern. Slab loads are assumed to travel to the columns by bending of the allocated bands. Actually, the spandrels, due to the unbalanced bending moments transmitted to them, rotate and carry the reactions to the columns partly by torsion. Diagonal torsion cracks then appear in the face of the spandrel section, especially if a deep beam is used. Such rotation has been known to push the masonry facing out of position and form horizontal cracks in the mortar jointing, with subsequent rain infiltration into the building. Spandrels must be designed to resist such torsional strains, or be braced across the ends to prevent rotation.

While employed by concrete contractors in the mid-1920's, the author was asked to explain and correct the frequent diagonal cracks on the exterior face of spandrel beams in flat slab buildings. The recommended solution, which was accepted and proved successful, was to eliminate the deep spandrels and substitute a slab band, no deeper than 1½ times the slab thickness. Such a band was much wider than the spandrel beam and, with longitudinal steel located in all four corners tied togther with closed hoops not more than 12 in. on centers, gave the necessary torsional resistance, and no cracks developed.

Incompatibility of deformation caused some cracks in precast prestressed louver slabs set into grooves of concrete piers in a unique and economical retaining wall in New York City. The embedded parts of the precast units were roughened to get better bond in the grouted grooves. A rigid connection resulted and when the wall was backfilled, the slabs deflected but the ends were held rigid and the face of the piers in front of the grooves cracked vertically. The pier deflection was small but at right angles in direction to that of the slabs. Reconstruction with a flexible filler corrected the trouble. Similar torsional action causes corners of roof slabs to curl and distort roof flashing and to crack exterior faces of exterior columns.

Storage bins designed for wall tension as a resistance to internal grain or liquid pressure must be free to expand at the contact with rigid base and roof slabs or foundation mat. As Mensch[44] pointed out, tank bottoms are highly vulnerable to failures, even if the shell is prestressed. Similar freedom must be provided at the junction between adjacent bins whether circular or rectangular, as is described by Vandegrift.[45] This kind of resistance to expansion explained the diagonal cracking in a large prestressed concrete pressure main near the joints which were grouted into precast concrete sleeves. The expansion of the pipe, as pressure was built up, was restrained near the ends by the rigid sleeves. The trouble disappeared when the joints were caulked with elastic material in place of the cement grout.

Elastic cracking is usually of a minor nature resulting only in leaks or unsightly appearance, but it can become a structural problem. One place where elastic cracking is quite noticeable is in the watertightness of parking garage floors. With the necessary long spans and with budget limitations usually requiring a minimum construction cost, leaky floors are very common.

In a garage in New York used for storage of expensive cars, considerable damage to paint finish from leakage through the floors resulted in a lawsuit where the "proximate" cause was argued at length. The investigation disclosed that in the steel fame with concrete slab, cracks appeared prominently in two lines in every second span. The cause was simple. To save steel weight, the beams were designed as continuous over two supports and with short suspended spans hanging from the ends of the cantilevers. The designer chose the length of the cantilevers so that the same beam section was sufficient under full live load for the continuous span and for the suspended span. The steel was bolted and then anchored by the concrete slab and beam encasement. The joint did not come at the point of inflection of a continuous frame; the slab cracked at the point of junction. It was shown that the curve of deformation of the steel system formed a discontinuity at the junction of cantilever and suspended span, and the cracks resulted as a normal consequence. The contractor won his defense.

Two-way reinforced uniform depth slabs seem to serve garage use requirements better than rigid bents of concrete or steel with thin one-way slabs between them. Variation in loading plus creep from aging make mandatory the addition of steel mesh in the top of the slab in all unreinforced areas. The dishing of the flat slabs is probably less troublesome than the cracking in the thin slabs along the contact with the rigid girders.

Using a bending moment diagram as the sole criterion for the amount and length of reinforcement results in a structure with no surplus strength to resist creep and plastic flow. A carefully designed waffle slab for a four-story school building at a military establishment built in 1950 showed such large slab deflections by 1955 that a complete steel frame was introduced to guarantee the safety of the floors. The work had been performed under the most careful and continuous inspection, yet dishing of the slabs was apparent before the floor finish was applied, and deflections continued to increase. The steel bars were of minimum length as required for computed moment with insufficient anchorage for the ends if the moment diagram changed under unbalanced loadings. A considerable amount of additional deflection seemed to come from slippage at the ends of the bars.

TEMPERATURE AND SHRINKAGE PROBLEMS

Although few examples of actual collapse can be attributed to temperature and shrinkage* stresses, failure in the form of objectionable cracking and spalling in concrete structures results from lack of freedom to modify dimensions with temperature changes and from aging. Cracks in continuous concrete structures cannot be entirely avoided, but it is possible through suitable reinforcement to make the individual cracks exceedingly small. The ratio of steel to concrete required for this purpose is relatively high, and where costs become prohibitive, expansion or contraction joints are introduced. Shrinkage distress can also be reduced by careful selection of mix proportions and curing methods.

"Safety is, of course, a prime consideration," as the *Engineering News-Record* remarked,† "but good engineering also calls for pro-

---

* "Shrinkage" and "swelling" designate the change in volume due to variation in moisture content of the concrete, as distinguished from contraction and expansion due to temperature changes.

† From an editorial, V. 164, No. 5, Feb. 4, 1960, p. 100.

visions that preclude structural damage at a minimum of cost, and that
are no more harmful than the damage they seek to prevent. . . . Undoubtedly more test data are needed to shed additional light on thermal behavior of structures so that they need not be under- or over-
designed for temperature effects. But there also appears to be evidence
that all engineers are not yet putting to use all the information now
available."

Because of the thermal insulation afforded by the exterior concrete
to its inner volume and because of the nonuniform rates of shrinkage in elements of different thickness and shape, the dimensional
changes are not entirely linear. Rotational displacements result and
seriously affect brittle masonry surfacing, windows, and door frames.
The differential shrinkage between thick and thin reinforced concrete
members in intimate contact can cause an eccentric pull on the members, and this is the usual reason for the cracks forming in slabs connecting to heavy griders. R. F. Blanks[46] presented some data on this
subject and showed the results of tests by Pickett in measuring the
coefficient of shrinkage at age of 9 months for various thicknesses:

1½ in. thick	720×10^{-6}
3 in. thick	700×10^{-6}
6 in. thick	580×10^{-6}
12 in. thick	330×10^{-6}

In addition to such shrinkage strains which introduce large tensile
stresses within a concrete mass, there are stresses from temperature
differences which compound the effect. The average thermal coefficient
for reinforced concrete is 0.0000055 per deg F change. For an elastic
modulus of 5,000,000 psi, each degree change induces a stress of 27.5
psi. If no reinforcement is provided across the section, it takes only
a few degrees temperature change to result in stresses in excess of the
maximum tensile resistance of plain concrete. Addition of uniformly
distributed and continuous reinforcement is always specified for floor
and roof slabs, but it is seldom required for beams and griders. Even
the minimum 0.25 percent requirement* if applied to all concrete sections would prevent possible shear failure of totally unreinforced surfaces.

Older literature[47] suggested a reinforcement minimum of 0.3 percent of the cross section to prevent cracking from shrinkage and tem-

---

* This is the minimum required for slabs with plain bars, according to "Building
Code Requirements for Reinforced Concrete (ACI 318-63)," Section 807. Where
deformed bars are used, minimum requirements are less.

perature, but even this amount has not always prevented formation of cracks. In 1933 Dreyer[48] reported experiments supporting Vetter's conclusion[49] that at least 0.65 percent longitudinal steel was needed to prevent unsightly cracks or leaks.

MOKELUMNE FLUME STUDY, CALIFORNIA—1928–29[48]

Since troublesome cracking had appeared in flumes with 0.3 percent transverse reinforcement, the Pacific Gas and Electric Co. set up an experimental flume section subject to actual use conditions before beginning construction of its 20 mile long Mokelumne flume. The 1600-ft experimental flume was 10 ft wide, 7 ft deep, with sidewalls and floor an average of 6 in. thick. It was divided into four 400-ft sections, with 0.27, 0.31. 0.47, and 0.65 percent, respectively, of longitudinal steel; there were no expansion joints.

The section was inspected while carrying water in September, 1928, and comparative crack size and amount of leakage were noted. At that time, the section having 0.25 percent longitudinal wall reinforcement showed cracks which developed leaks sufficient to cause water to drip from a shoulder left by the outside forms at the bottom of the wall. These main cracks were spaced in general from 15 to 25 ft apart. In the section having 0.31 percent reinforcement, the main cracks were spaced generally from 15 to 35 ft apart, the leaks were smaller, and, in many cases, the wall was only damp to the bottom. In the section having 0.47 percent wall reinforcement, the main cracks averaged about 25 ft apart, and the wall in the majority of cases was only wet or damp. The section having 0.65 percent wall reinforcement showed very small cracks 75 to 100 ft apart.

The following spring, another inspection was made. It was observed that in the section having 0.27 percent longitudinal reinforcement, the leaks in general had increased and one (which appeared to be at the end of a day's placement) had reached a flow of approximately 0.5 gal. per min. Several leaks showed efflorescence and, in one case, disintegration, probably caused by ice and frost during the winter. An increase in leaks and damp spots was also observed in the section having 0.31 percent reinforcement, although to a lesser degree. In both the aforementioned sections the amount of leakage was considered undesirable for such structures as reinforced concrete flumes when severe winters prevail. The leakage in the first section could endanger certain types of soil foundations, where bench flumes are concerned.

The last two sections, having 0.47 percent and 0.65 percent reinforcement, showed satisfactory conditions, outside of an increase in number of sweat spots. The last section had few surface cracks for this type of construction.

Concluding that at least 0.65 percent longitudinal steel was needed—if reinforcement alone was to control cracking—it was decided to place expansion (contraction) joints with copper waterstop at 20-ft intervals, and to use 0.2 percent longitudinal steel.

Roof expansion troubles caused by high temperatures were analyzed relatively early in the history of concrete construction, as the next two cases show.

Reservoir, Colombo, Ceylon—1885-1890[50]

In 1885, a concrete reservoir holding 10 million gallons of water was built in Colombo, Ceylon. Wall faces were vertical inside and 5 on 12 batter outside; the floor was 12 in. thick and a concrete slab covered the 30 ft deep box. When the reservoir was filled in 1885 to a depth of 24 ft, cracks were noted near the corners. After repairs and adding another foot of floor concrete, refilling in 1886 to a depth of 28 ft again produced cracks near the top of the walls, which traveled to the ground level in 15 minutes.

Sir John Fowler, a past president of the Institution of Civil Engineers (England), was consulted and analyzed the cause as expansion in the high temperatures of the area. He recommended cutting strips out of the walls and inserting brick piers covered with asphalt, as well as an asphalt lining for the entire reservoir. After his suggestions were followed, the reservoir was filled again in 1889. Once more cracks appeared at the corners, but the lining prevented leakage.

Since stress calculations indicated these cracks could not have been caused by insufficient resistance to the water pressure alone, tests were made to determine the effects of temperature change. Daily oscillation of the tops of the walls measured 0.005 to 0.01 in., with the greatest movement at the northeast corner. It was concluded that the thrust of the expanding roof was the cause. After the roof and walls were covered with earth, no further cracking occurred. This 5-year history of repair exemplifies British determination to make a design work.

Reservoir, Madrid, Spain—1905[51]

A reservoir was built in Madrid of reinforced concrete 22 ft deep, to hold 127 million gallons. It was to be in four compartments of equal size. The roof consisted of a series of parabolic arches resting on beams 20 in. deep. The arches were uniformly 4 in. thick with a rise of 23 in. and a span of 19 ft. The beams were supported by 12 in. square columns 27 ft high, and formed a continuous length of 700 ft over two compartments. When the first of the four boxes was completed, and the roof covered with 31 in. of sand, it was noted that the girders were deflected and the columns were being pushed by an expansion of the total length. The deformations were maximum at about 3 p.m. and decreased at night. In about a week, some columns broke and the roof collapsed (June 6, 1905).

Failure of the design to take into account the considerable expansion and contraction of the horizontal girders due to temperature change brought about the failure. Columns were not strong enough to resist the lateral forces caused by temperature changes; they were poorly anchored, too high for their small cross-section, and had no lateral support.

Considering a more recent case, thermal and shrinkage stresses probably were an important consideration in the failure of rigid frames at Wilkins and Robins air force bases described on p. 25. These rigid frames consisted of six 67-ft continuous spans with an expansion joint in the third span from one end. The expansion joints apparently did not operate and the 400-ft length was a single unit as far as temperature and shrinkage effect were concerned. Both collapses came at a season of the year when the net heat absorption gain was about maximum (night loss having been less than the day gain). The 1955 failure was after a most unusual hot spell.

Expansion Freedom Needed

Normal temperatures permit large structures to absorb enough heat so that surfaces spall, plane areas become curved, and even structural defects occur. The athletic stadiums are a good example of the necessity for providing free space for expansion. This is evident in all stadiums, whether steel or concrete framed. During a detailed investigation of the Polo Grounds in New York in 1940, the magnitude and intensity of the movements was pointed out by the loud and continuous creaking of the structure in the early mornings as the sun started to warm it up. Numerous stadiums are today undergoing continuous repair programs. An inspection of almost any of them shows a shortage of open joints to permit expansion; often such freedom must be three dimensional if excessive and expensive maintenance is to be avoided.

Lateral expansion of structures often causes brick covering to push and crack. The cracks never close completely with colder weather,

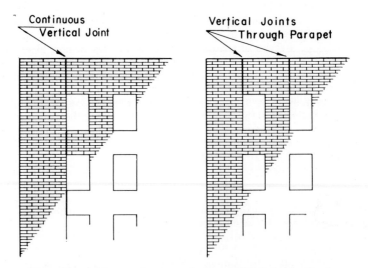

Figure 3.11—Brick-covered concrete frames of New York City Housing Authority projects have a continuous vertical joint at the first window edge of each end of wall surface (left) to control cracking. In another region, vertical joints from top of top-story window up and through parapet (right) for the first and second openings back from each corner have been used to help keep parapets plumb.

some dust always finds its way into the crevice, and subsequent ex-pansions increase the crack size. To control this cracking, in the New York City Housing Authority projects, all brick-covered concrete frames are built with vertical continuous joints at the first window edge of each end of a wall surface. This does not eliminate the expansion, but at least stops the cracking of the brick since the opening follows a con-tinuous mortar line.

Better control of internal temperature in buildings has increased the range of temperature differences at the roof level. Change in size of the roof slab where rigid attachment is made to the walls must result in cracked walls, usually at about the head of the top-story window since the resisting wall section is suddenly reduced at this level. Usual expansion of the roof indicates itself in many buildings by such crack-ing with accompanying leakage, wall staining and heat losses in the top story. Some designs call for a projecting brick course at this level to shade the crack.

Roof Terrace Expansion

Expansion of roof terraces, usually of quarry tile, when insufficient expan-sion joints are provided as a border, will push out the parapet walls. One such condition was the subject of a correction procedure designed by the author. The owner built a tile deck on the roof of an apartment house on West 71st Street in New York and did not provide expansion joints. After a few days of hot weather, a complaint came from the top-story occupants that daylight was coming through the walls above window level. The report was not exaggerated. The parapet had moved out over 2 in. and the walls fractured along each window line and rotated on the supporting lintel angles. An expensive reconstruction under very dangerous conditions was rushed to completion before the driving rains of the autumn storms, which would have flooded the apartments.

During the construction of the Mulford Houses, a low cost project in Yonkers, N.Y., in 1939, it was suggested that a 1-in. gap be pro-vided between the face of the roof spandrel and the brick covering. This was accomplished by inserting a strip of plywood against the con-crete and removing it after the brick facing reached roof level. Although the parapet, 12-in. solid brickwork, covers the gap, the desired free-dom of movement seems to have been accomplished; no cracks formed in this project.

Where the designer expects freedom of motion, longitudinal or rota-tional, the structural detail must be properly designed and executed to permit facility of motion; otherwise distress will result. Cracked sur-faces near apparent expansion joints are usually the result of a frozen joint, either discontinuous for architectural reasons or improperly constructed (Figure 3.12). For example, piers on which concrete girders were designed to slide as an expansion separation between long span garage roof and adjoining apartment building were found to have seats which had not even been troweled smooth, and cracked piers indicated the locations of such deficiencies in workmanship.

DETAILING AND DRAFTING

There has been a gradual but persistent tendency for the design drawing to show maximum reinforcement conditions and leave to the detailers the development of laps and splices, the decision of where to stop the bars, and other decisions which should be part of the design. Errors that creep in are easily overlooked in the checking of shop drawings. The European practice, as well as that of many public works projects here, is to detail all the rods on the design sheets. This practice has merit, in spite of the shortage of technical help, since the over-all labor required is actually reduced, even though it means that a design office will do fewer jobs in a year.

Does any design office leave to the contractor the job of determining actual dimensions of the concrete work? An editorial[52] questioning whether the standards for detailing could be blamed for some of the "concrete structures that have fared badly" brought forth vehement professional denial of any correlation. It is important that details follow a recognized standard and that everyone use the same symbols

Figure 3.12—Designer's intention was foiled by this inadequately formed expansion joint which did not provide adequate relief. As a result, the wall cracked about 18 in. away from the desired control point.

Figure 3.13—Collapse of this rigid frame bent in Coronado, California, was attributed to poor detailing practice. Failure line followed an unreinforced concrete section of the frame.

and notation. In slabs with straight steel in top and bottom, it has been found expedient and economical to prepare separate detail sheets for the top steel and for the bottom steel. The layers are separately installed, and this procedure eliminates possible errors or misunderstanding.

When a design is not carried to completion with details consistently analyzed and carefully delineated, unexpected things happen, as some of the following examples indicate. Cracks, spalls, disintegration at connections, deflections, and deformations appear without apparent cause. Areas of high stress are particularly vulnerable to flaws resulting from inadequate or improper detailing.

Splices, Hinges, Joints

Reinforcement splices, hinges, expansion joints, and construction joints must be clearly and carefully represented, leaving no room for misinterpretation in the field by the builder, so that the structure acts as the designer intended.

RIGID FRAME BENT, NAVAL AMPHIBIOUS BASE, CORONADO, CALIFORNIA—1954

One 40-ton bent of a 3300-man mess hall for the Naval Amphibious Base at Coronado, Calif., collapsed suddenly Feb. 6, 1954 (Figure 3.13). The precast reinforced bent was 18 ft high at the outside, with a 16-ft clearance at the middle of its 67½-ft span. There was no dead load except the weight of the 20 in. thick bent itself.

Improper detailing of the reinforcing steel at the haunch was blamed for the failure, according to data released by the navy.[53] Detailing of the original plans, plus the shop drawings for reinforcement placement, was such that an unreinforced plane existed at the point of maximum moment, where

the designer had located a splice in order to reduce cost of shipping fabricated reinforcement (Figure 3.14). The designer stated that his *intention*
had been that top reinforcing bars bending around the corner be intermeshed
with vertical bars. Unfortunately this intention was not conveyed to the
fabricator, and the designer made no inspection of the reinforcing steel
during construction.

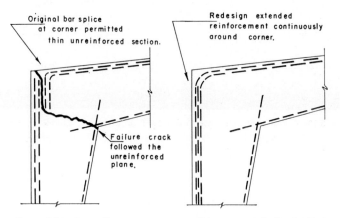

Figure 3.14—Bar splice at outer corner of bent as originally detailed
was responsible for collapse; sketch shows crack location. At right is
revised detail which assured continuous reinforcement at the critical
corner (not to scale).

The design was corrected by moving the splice 10 ft from the point of
maximum tension and by welding, and by adding shear reinforcement around
the corner (Figure 3.14); all of the bents of this design were replaced at a
cost of about $60,000.

It was pointed out in a number of discussions following the Coronado frame failure that every lapped bar introduced shearing stress
in the concrete within the splice length. The intensities of the stress
in the bars and the minimum splice lengths specified in codes are not
safe if splices are permitted at locations of high tensile or compressive
steel stresses. Bent bars carrying high stress induce a diagonal resultant in the concrete; the amount and direction is easily determined by
the requirement of static equilibrium at the point of bend. Many
stairway-landing spans show spalled concrete on the underface at the
junction of landing and stair soffits where the tension steel is bent
with no provision for resisting the outward resultant. The detail of
splicing the bars at this point, carrying the tensile steel of the plat-
form and of the stair separately into the concrete mass, is better, but
must be studied to avoid possible shear failure through unreinforced
sections.

In large span frames, the concentration of bars makes proper concreting difficult, especially at the splices where the number of bars is doubled. To reduce the number of different bar lengths, splices are often not staggered.

In a large span concrete frame, the bridge carrying the New York, New Haven, and Hartford Railroad over the Hudson River Parkway, Pelham, N.Y., where welding was not feasible, the bars were detailed with upset and threaded ends and internally threaded steel pipe sleeves at splices. The saving in splice material, tie wire labor, and the lower concrete placing costs practically paid for the threading and sleeves. However, all main bars were continuous and the design was easily executed in the field.

The splice problem also exists at the bottom of many multistory columns where the concentration of spliced bars makes it uncertain what concrete encasement can be obtained; often the lower bars are bent inward to provide space for the upper bars. Frequently, as in the case of the Pennsylvania office building in Washington, D.C., this difficulty can be overcome by welding the bars at about 6 in. above the top of footings. The welding cost there was no more than the value of the lap lengths saved, but the time factor was serious; welding rate slowed up the schedule, and the planned welding at upper story splices was abandoned.

PRESTRESSED ROOF BEAM, OMAHA, NEBRASKA—1957

Failure of a roof beam in Omaha in 1957 resulted from improper splicing of prestressing steel. The beam was one of five 100-ft post-tensioned concrete members, erected partly prestressed, with final tensioning after roof load was applied. About two hours after final stressing but with the tendons not yet grouted, the beam cracked and buckled upward about 12 in. at midspan. The prestressing was by 14 end-anchored bars, draped in a vertical curve. Because available bars were only 80 ft long all of them were spliced and, since further stress was to be applied, they were laid within sheaths which were 3 inches in diameter to make room for the splices. Seven of the 14 bars were spliced at the same point, where failure occurred. The reduction in concrete cross section was too large for the induced total load, and compression failure resulted.

Supports of heavy load concentrations on pins, hinges, and grillages must be detailed for all loading conditions. Concrete rigid frames designed for flexible hinges require special provisions for the high compressive and shear forces at the hinge.

Balog[54] reported the failure of 17 three-hinged rigid frames in Austria in 1938. The 89.4-ft span frames collapsed immediately following the formwork removal. The bearing hinges contained ten intersecting bars, spirally tied, precast into 8x9-in. blocks. These blocks were set into the footings and extended 20 in. into the frame columns. To assure hinge action, a 2 in.

thick felt layer covered with tar paper was placed around the intersecting bars at the top of the footing. After concrete was carefully placed around these hinge blocks, column portions of the bent were concreted; a ½ to ¾-in. felt gap remained between the footings and the column bases of the frames which collapsed. In 17 similar frames which did not fail, the wet concrete compacted the water-saturated felt completely, leaving no gap between columns and footing.

The 17 frames failed a short distance above the bearing hinges. Bond between precast hinge blocks and column was impaired, and concrete encasement of the blocks was not strong enough to take full dead load. When forms were removed, the 26 in. square concrete section broke. Use of the precast unit was an error; continuous construction at the location of these three hinges would have resulted in a satisfactory structure.

Joints—The designer should indicate location of both construction joints and expansion joints. Badly located construction joints (whether from lack of detailed instructions to the builder or from ignorance of proper design) have caused failures. Even with continuous reinforcement, construction joints should be restricted to areas of minimum shear.

The effect of shrinkage on the geometry of an assembly of precast members must be considered in the design and in the details of jointing. High-early-strength concrete, obtained with special cements, calcium chloride, and steam curing (as might well be the case for prestressed members) is subject to shrinkage over longer periods than are normal mix concretes.[*]

Prestressed Concrete Details

Specialized knowledge is required for designing details for prestressed concrete installations. Direct copy of satisfactory details from structural steel or conventional reinforced concrete design is not advisable. Shoe and bearing details, for example, must be designed to provide for the shape and length changes which occur when prestressed beams are loaded, as the following case demonstrates.

Several long precast beams, up to 113 ft, for a skew bridge crossing had been detailed with steel bearing plates to be anchored to the abutment seats. The post-tensioning induced camber in the beams, according to design, with straight profiles planned under full dead load of the stringers, deck slab, and paving. However, the beams were erected in the abutments without any of this additional dead load, and their weight alone was insufficient to reduce the camber. Great care had been taken to set the bearing plates on the abutment seats in perfect position with the anchor bolts exactly to fit the templates of the concrete beam ends, but of course the ends did not fit.

[*] Some recent data of interest on shrinkage appeared in articles by T. C. Powers and M. Mamillan in *Revue des Materiaux* (Paris), No. 545, Feb. 1961.

Not only were the beams apparently short, but the shoe plates were slightly rotated. Repairs had to be made with the 80-ton beams suspended in the air from two cranes—an expensive and time-consuming operation.

In prestressing work, the highest stress concentration develops under the bearing plate of a post-tensioned anchorage. At this point the best concrete strength is required together with some hoop or spiral reinforcement to resist lateral expansion under the high stress. However, the bearing plate, often with attached anchors, in combination with cable or rod sheath, stirrups, and hoops frequently interferes with getting a dense concrete. Usually there is no room for a vibrator and compaction of the concrete mix depends on manual rodding and tamping "as far as possible." Sometimes the result is not sufficient, as in the case of one very large prestressed concrete viaduct project in New York. There, the bearing plates set in the web face of the outer girders for cross-tensioning the roadway width crushed the web when jacking was applied. Concrete behind the plate was found quite porous; there were too many steel items (as noted above) behind the plate to permit a proper filling of the web with concrete.

Similar complications with bearing plate details occurred in a fine monumental building in Philadelphia described below.

PHILADELPHIA POLICE ADMINISTRATION BUILDING, PHILADELPHIA, PENNSYLVANIA—1961[13]

The main floor consisted of circular sectors with field post-tensioning required to join the pretensioned castings. The narrow end of the sectors contained two separate bearing areas, each 7x14 in., with a total of four stressed rods. The bearing plates were at the top of the casting with little clear distance along three edges. With each rod stressed to 130,000 lb, the average unit pressure under the bearing plate was 4000 psi on a concrete mix designed for 5000 psi. With only the upper rod stressed to full value, the edge pressure was higher, depending on the closeness of contact. Some localized shear failures occurred in back of the bearing plates. The result was a complete stoppage of work, with a tentative order to demolish all or part of the structure built at that time.

The order was later rescinded, but only after extensive tests, inspections, and arguments. In the broken end bearings, it was found that two small steel stirrups had been omitted in the plant manufacture, "to provide space for the concrete." Added concrete strength was obtained by filling the gap between the two separate bearing areas, a space which had been left for possible vertical pipes in the wall. After the spalled and cracked ends had been rebuilt, all remaining post-tensioning was performed in a two-step procedure, each rod being stressed to 50 percent of its desired load, then the other 50 percent added in sequence. Since the rods were too closely spaced to provide clearance for jacks, this required four operations, but it reduced the high local eccentric stress concentrations during the stressing.

The project is now completed and a credit to both the architect and engineer, but a great deal of trouble and unfavorable publicity could have been avoided by providing greater bearing areas with more easily executed details.

Drafting Errors

The drawing is the universal graphic language used to advise the builder of what the designer has deemed to be sufficient. No matter how good or complete the design, it is of no value if it is not completely and correctly shown on the drawings. Presentation is fully as important as the design as far as proper construction and protection against failure are concerned.

Every step through which a design passes allows chance for error; the drafting room is no exception. Graphical presentation of a design should be done by qualified persons. The importance of checking by someone with enough experience to recognize errors both in design and drafting cannot be overemphasized.

Collapse of a reinforced concrete retaining wall at Manhasset, New York, was caused by careless drafting.[55]

The design called for 1¼-in. square bars vertically and the draftsman placed the "1" of the "1¼" directly on a dimension line. Since the "1" was covered, the drawing appeared to call for ¼-in. steel (Figure 3.15). The smaller steel was supplied and installed. Total collapse started as soon as the wall was backfilled.

It is a strange coincidence that no one questioned the bars that were delivered and installed. The design had been checked by an outside engineer upon request of the local building department inspector before a permit was issued and the design was approved. Shop drawings of the reinforcement were prepared but there was no record of any checking or approval; yet these shop details were used in the actual construction as a correct guide.

A similar drafting error was brought to light in the investigation of large stone facing units which rotated out of position on a monumental court building in New York. The stone was designed to be supported on suspended steel angles with lead pads under each angle. The corner was carefully detailed in the contract drawings with angle and lead plate extending to 2 in. from the edge of the stone and the rest of the joint caulked. The shop drawing had a dimension shown as 1·2½ (meant to be 1 ft 2½ in.) from edge of stone to center of corner columns. This was misread as 12½ in., and the steel angles were all ordered and installed 2 in. short, *i.e.*, 4 in. from the corner with no

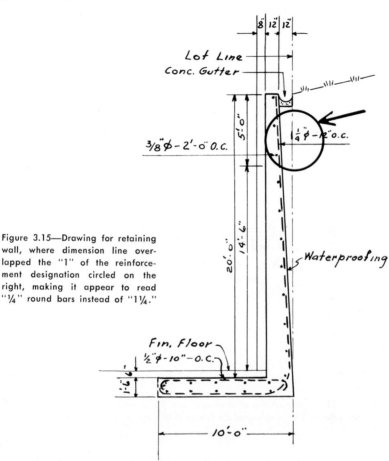

Figure 3.15—Drawing for retaining wall, where dimension line overlapped the "1" of the reinforcement designation circled on the right, making it appear to read "¼" round bars instead of "1¼."

lead plate in the horizontal joint of the corner stone. The hard mortar joint gripped the corners and the large stone sheets turned outward.

An outright error was blamed for failure of a sedimentation basin at Sacramento, Calif., June 24, 1924.[56] The next tank was empty and unbalanced pressure carried away about 80 ft of a 19 ft high wall. The tank had been properly designed to withstand dewatering in either basin, but the tracer had shown only one-fourth of the required steel in the wall that failed. Errors like this should be detected when the drawings are checked.

Another oversight, which was not discovered in time, proved responsible for diagonal cracks at the ends of cantilevers from the main span of a six-lane highway viaduct in New York.

Cracks appeared on one side only and were correlated with the use of the outer roadway for concrete trucks in the finishing operations on the pavement. The design was checked and found sufficient for the specified loadings including trucking except that the top steel for the cantilevers was stopped suddenly at 40 diameters inside the inner face of the pier (Figure 3.16). This error, later investigation revealed, had been found by the designer and the correction noted on the design sheets; the correction never

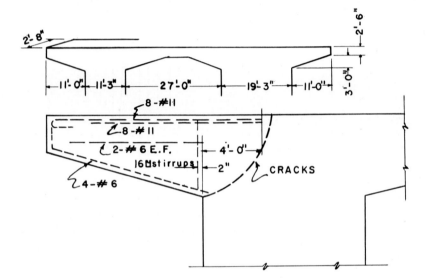

Figure 3.16—Cutting off top steel of cantilever 40 diameters inside pier face caused cracks. Error had been corrected on design sheets, but the change was never carried to the drawings.

was carried to the drawings. When trucks were run on the other outer lane, corresponding cracks appeared in that cantilever. (This test was not performed until all the cantilevers were shored.) Correction was by the addition of post-tensioned cables on both sides of each bent, bearing through end steel billets, to add compressive stress in the axial direction. The cables were then encased in pneumatically applied concrete to form shoulder projections on the sides of the bents.

For simplicity in detailing and bar installation, it is often expedient to use the same reinforcement for a roof slab as in the typical floor of a multistory building. This tendency may explain why, in another school building, the main reinforcement over an interior support of the floors was incorrectly copied from the design notes and the much lighter reinforcement of the roof design was shown and used. Although this was only one of several noncompliances discovered in the investigation, it may have had a considerable influence on the resulting large slab deflections found after the form was removed. As a correction, a 4 in. thick cap slab was introduced after shoring the deflected slab and wedging it upward and adding high strength steel wire mesh welded to studs shot into the concrete over part of the deflected span and the complete (shorter) adjacent span. A considerable portion of the unwanted deflection was eliminated and a full scale load test showed good composite action of the unusual post-stressing procedure.

ERRORS IN ASSUMED LOADINGS

Even though the stress analysis and resulting design for any structure are correctly completed in every detail, the design can be no better than the accuracy of the assumed loadings. Most ordinary loadings have been studied and codified to such an extent that the designer can be reasonably confident of his selected magnitude. However, occasional failures do result from loadings which the designer did not, or could not, anticipate. New types of design for commonly used structures, or conventional designs of special purpose structures, may call for a more thorough investigation of expected loads. The designer of precast members must also consider possible lateral loads arising during delivery and erection (see handling, erection, p. 89).

Wind Load

The true pressure pattern of wind forces is generally well known. Failures in hurricane or tornado storms are usually considered the result of economically expendable designs. Complete design against a direct hit by a tornado is not ordinarily feasible, but certain minimum requirements are necessary to protect adjoining structures. One of them is to provide for the rapid change in barometric pressure. Closed attic spaces are especially vulnerable and blow-out of roofs or walls can be prevented by proper louver arrangement.

Wind pressures blamed for structural failures are often accompanied by suction effects.

The collapse of a one-story factory at Union City, Tenn., in 1952 occurred during a wind of no more than 30 mph. Complete investgation showed no design deficiencies. Wood roof trusses were sufficient and properly braced and connected to columns. There was however a reported barometric pressure drop to below 29 in. More recently, a suck-out of entire windows—glass, frame, and anchors—from the upper floors of a new Manhattan skyscraper occurred during the passing of a low pressure front accompained by 75 mph wind. Similar failures of sections of lightweight panel walls have been reported in New Orleans and Philadelphia.

Snow Load

Inadequate planning for actual snow loading would not be expected in "snow country"; yet as recently as 1959 there was a collapse of a plank and wood truss roof over a skating rink at Huntsville, Ont., under a load of 16 in. of snow. Failure occurred without warning during an exhibition curling game. A witness reported complete collapse in 15 sec; the roof fell vertically without damage to the 18-in. concrete supporting walls.

A study of actual snow loadings on ground and roofs from 1956 to 1959 was made by the National Research Council of Canada[57] to check the validity of loadings specified in the 1953 National Building Code of Canada. Although it was generally found that snow loads on roofs are less than on the ground, yet certain roof shapes and conditions, such as an entrance canopy set into an angle of a building, tend to catch snow depths far greater than the average ground cover.

Snow loadings must take into account the possible weight of rain saturation of the snow blanket. The present National Building Code of Canada specifies 60 psf over a considerable area of eastern Canada, and up to 90 psf for Labrador and the mountainous provinces.

Water Load

Unexpected loading often comes from water. Level roofs with or without designed water layers are often overloaded when drains become clogged or frozen.

An unusual difficulty was experienced with a fluted metal deck roof that was exposed to melting snow before the roofing was installed. The flutes filled with water and the deck deflected enough under added rainfall after sealing the roof, to break the seam welds and cause a great deal of damage when the trapped water fell on the work below.

Accumulated water was one cause of the collapse of the flat prestressed cafetorium roof at the Orlando, Fla., school described on p. 37. During a torrential rain, water accumulated on the deflected roof deck, and ponding was increased by runoff from an adjoining pitched roof. The ponding brought about more deflection, and progressively increasing load on the slab roof. Collapse of a roof section and supporting block walls followed.

Unpredictable Loadings

A steel and concrete roof covering an 86,000 sq ft box factory in Mexico City collapsed in 1958. The structure consisted of concrete-covered metal decking on steel trusses supported by concrete block walls and reinforced concrete columns. Failure was sudden and reportedly resulted from vibrations induced by heavy machinery.

The 24-mile concrete causeway over Lake Pontchartrain in Louisiana was struck by a floating barge during construction in March, 1956. A similar accident again occurred in January, 1960, after the structure was in use. In both cases, two deck section spans were knocked out. The designer could not be reasonably expected to design a structure to withstand such loadings. Pier and bulkhead structures in northern areas should, however, be designed to resist the force of floating ice if lateral displacement, as has occurred in the Hudson River, is to be avoided.

The sinking loss and damage to preassembled pontoon sections of the Lake Washington floating bridge across Hood Canal in 1959 was attributed to unplugged holes in the sidewalls a short distance above the water level. Water entered the pontoons either from wave action or as a result of tipping when a barge snagged the anchor line.

CHANGES IN USE OF STRUCTURE LEAD TO FAILURE

Long-standing structures may be used for various purposes throughout their lifetime, either with or without structural alterations, but frequently with loadings considerably different from those contemplated by the original designer. Unless careful regard is given to the carrying capacity of the structure as originally designed, unfortunate failures may occur.

Failures often result from careless alterations to existing structures. Usually new floor surfacings and hung ceilings add to the dead loads, but the worst offense is the cutting of new floor openings for vertical transportation and air conditioning ducts. Quite often, the original design drawings are not available and the revisions are made independently without regard to the effect on the existing framing.

Such failures occur in structures of all materials. Publicity is kept to a minimum, and as a result, lessons are lost. Even where collapse of a structure makes newspaper headlines with pictures and considerable published misinformation, the report of causes and reasons comes so late that no one is interested except the immediate family, and they do not feel like talking.

In 1946 a complete collapse of a building on Duane Street in lower Manhattan affected so many financial interests that it was necessary to determine the real causes.

DUANE STREET BUILDING, NEW YORK, N.Y.—1946

Under the author's direction, the wreckage of this building was taken apart floor by floor, and the contents of each floor weighed and the construction carefully inspected. Fortunately the failure occurred after all employees had gone home, and eventually the fact that there were no fatalities so impressed the various interested parties that each one took a share of the loss by agreement without litigation.

The photographs of the collapse (Figure 3.17) indicated a definite axis of the funnel of failure. This axis was traced down floor by floor and actually

Figure 3.17—Duane Street building collapse showing "funnel of failure"; funnel axis traced down floor by floor pointed to origin of failure.

pointed to a structural weakness which was the cause. The building had been used as a part of a large department store, built about 1870, with open light wells in the center area of each section. Sometimes, as many may remember, these wells were enclosed by glass panels. When the building was converted to commercial use, someone had removed the panels and completed the wood flooring without changing or adding to the beam supports. On the first floor a paper cutting machine was found partly resting on this added flooring, which had been supported on 2x4's to fill in the old light well. A load of paper delivered on the day of the collapse surrounded the machine. The floor couldn't take the concentration and sagged downward carrying everything with it.

A nine-story apartment house in Rome split from roof to foundation in September, 1959, as a result of loading unanticipated in the original design.[58] Crack width varied from 6 in. at lower levels to almost 30 in. at the top of the building. Damage to the 28-apartment structure was reported due to installation of 28 concrete water tanks of 80 gal. capacity on the roof, adding about 44 tons of load. With living space scarce, only the nine apartments in which the crack developed were vacated. Deep concrete beams were installed in the lobby to stiffen the structure, and glass rods were inserted in walls and partitions to give warning of further movement as a signal to vacate the premises.

The much more tragic collapse described below occurred the same month at Barletta, Italy. Fifty-eight lives were lost as the result of an ill-considered addition to an existing structure.

APARTMENT BUILDING, BARLETTA, ITALY—1959

A five-story apartment structure collapsed at Barletta, Italy in mid-September, 1959, about 5 months after its completion, leaving a toll of 58 dead and 13 injured. A four-story addition of reinforced concrete and brick construction had been built on top of what was once a one-story garage. A city employee reported[59] that the city engineer's report showed the foundation was capable of holding only two additional stories.

As a result of the ensuing investigation and trial, two builders, the structural engineer, and a city official were sentenced to prison terms ranging from 15 to 18 years. The prosecutor established that the building was not evacuated, although the defendants had foreseen that collapse was imminent. Cracks appeared in one wall several days before the failure, and the contractor had tried to strengthen the wall with a reinforced concrete buttress.[60] This only further overloaded the foundation soil, redistributed the wall stresses, and speeded collapse, according to an expert witness for the prosecution.

4

Construction Problems
Leading to Failure

AMONG THE CONSTRUCTION CONDITIONS that cause failures are the following which are discussed in this chapter:

1. Inadequate over-all supervision and inspection
2. Poor mixing and placing practices
3. Cold and hot weather
4. Erection problems such as with lift slab and other precast units

Formwork collapses have been such a common and frequent cause of trouble during construction that they are treated separately in the following chapter.

Fortunately most failures of concrete structures occur either during the construction stage, or before the structures are fully in use. Ironically many a collapse comes as workers are concreting the roof slab or placing concrete near the top of a multistory structure,* when construction loads have reached a maximum on a structure whose strength is only partially developed.

It is the purpose of this chapter to discuss those failures whose primary cause is found in errors or deficiencies of the construction

---

* Speculating on why many failures occur so near the end of the job, M. C. Tuttle[61] of the Aberthaw Construction Co. wrote in 1912: "The average small contracting outfit does not have an accurate enough cost-keeping system to

process, whether they occur while construction is actually in progress or not. Naturally, some failures occur during the later life of a structure because of the way in which construction was handled, and some failures (like several discussed in Chapter 3) which occur during construction can be traced to flaws in the design. As previously mentioned, "failure" is used in the broad sense of noncompliance with the designer's intent or specifications, and includes defects of position, alignment, dimensions, wearing surfaces and the like, as well as partial or total collapse.

Since many cases involve several contributing causes, cases have been assigned to the various categories according to the author's judgment as to what was the most significant factor leading to failure. A few early cases presented first under a "multiple causes" heading demonstrate the compounding of problems that often occurred in the early days of concrete construction. In analyzing these failures, it is of course helpful to consider the state of development of concrete technology at that time, to realize that material strengths were often substantially lower than those available today, and that quality control, proportioning, and curing practices were far different from those now current.

EARLY CASES; MULTIPLE CAUSES

Pure carelessness or ignorance of the construction workers was the immediate cause of this first incident, but when an investigating commission was appointed a number of other undesirable practices were brought to light.

HOTEL, BASEL, SWITZERLAND—1901[62]

Complete collapse of one wing of a five-story beam-and-slab hotel structure occurred in Basel, Switzerland, Aug. 28, 1901. The investigating commission reported that masonry pillars resting on concrete footings at the basement level were supposed to support beams of the first floor. These pillars were not built first as they should have been; rather, the beam was temporarily supported on wooden bents. On the day of the collapse, the workmen were at last ready to build the masonry piers. However, instead of leaving the

---

show them, from time to time, as work progresses just what work is costing and how near it is coming to the estimate. As the work reaches a close, however, the simple total of the ledger shows them all too frequently that the work is costing them more than they are getting for it, with the result that at the end of the job there is a frantic effort to make economies of every sort, the most obvious economies being to use less cement and to hasten the drawing of forms, with the result that over and over again the building's collapse comes from some pure carelessness which could be readily avoided."

temporary wooden supports until the piers were ready, they removed them in order to build the masonry more conveniently. Removal of the bents left columns of the first floor unsupported except by the floor beam, and two hours after the removal, the building gave way.

Design of the structure was prepared in Paris, and the designing firm merely supplied plans and undertook no control of the field work. The local building department limited its control strictly to that prescribed by law, and the contractor in charge let the job "take its course," as the commission reported, with little or no system in the work.

Final conclusion of the investigating experts was that, although improper removal of temporary wooden supports triggered the failure, the following were also contributing causes: (1) insufficient dimensions of columns in the first story, together with lack of control of the contractors over the construction; (2) use of improper material (unwashed sand and gravel including material directly from the excavation); (3) careless construction of the concrete work (bottoms of the columns were poorly consolidated); (4) lack of tests of the cement and concrete; (5) lack of organization among the various subcontractors; and (6) haste in construction.

Multiple problems also were literally uncovered from the debris in the following case, although the collapse started when formwork was being removed.

EASTMAN KODAK COMPANY BUILDING, ROCHESTER, NEW YORK—1906

The two-story building, with brick veneer walls and reinforced concrete column, slab and girder framing was 134x169 ft in plan; the roof slab was of hollow tile with 4-in. reinforced beams between tiles. This was one of six similar structures, all being built by the same designer-contractor. *Engineering Record*[63] reported that the design had been changed from time to time to protect "secret" manufacturing processes of the company.

The building was near completion, and workmen were removing forms and shoring from a section of the northeast corner of the roof when roof and supporting columns fell, apparently without warning, over an area about 53x88 ft. The mezzanine floor below gave way over a 45x21-ft area, but the main floor withstood the shock of falling debris except for a 2 ft square hole punched by a falling girder. Four lives were lost and 15 men injured. Concrete of the roof slab was about three weeks old at the time of the accident (Nov. 21, 1906), and had been inspected the day before by the construction foreman, who pronounced it ready for form removal.[64]

Investigators engaged by the owner declared[65] early form removal was to blame: "Had the forms around the columns and sides of the large beams been first removed, and the supports under girders and floor construction left undisturbed for a period of at least four weeks longer, it is our opinion that you would have not experienced the slightest trouble." However, other inquiries into the failure disclosed many evidences of bad workmanship. Poor quality concrete, voids and exposed steel in girders, chips, leaves, sawdust, and blocks of wood in the columns—these were some of the defects mentioned. Column 47, which appeared to have failed first below the mezzanine floor, was of crumbly concrete, built smaller than the designed size, and had four reinforcing bars missing. (A nearby column appeared to have four extra bars!)

The coroner returned a verdict of criminal negligence against the contractor and the owner's assistant manager of works, attributing collapse to crushing of Column 47.[64] The coroner further concluded that "No steel-concrete structures can be considered safe unless some reliable man is absolutely responsible for putting the proper number of proper sized bars in the positions designated for them." He also suggested that allowable stress upon steel and concrete in construction "should be fixed by law."

The next incident attracted widespread interest and was the focus of controversial discussion in the engineering press because the building was of the then-new flat slab construction. Design theories were debated, but construction problems including cold weather, unstable shoring, and possible overloading of the roof played a part in the tragedy that took eight lives.

PRESTOLITE BUILDING, INDIANAPOLIS, INDIANA—1911

The three-story column and flat slab structure had originally been contracted as a two-story building, but during building, it was decided to add a third floor. The Indianapolis inspector had approved plans for the two-story building, but no permit was ever issued for the third floor.[66] Work on the cinder roof fill was in progress at the time of failure Dec. 6, 1911. The 70x88-ft building was completely wrecked, and the point of initial failure could not be precisely established. Leaning columns which remained suggested collapse inward toward a central starting point.

Engineering plans were provided by the steel supplier. Slabs were 8, 7, and 6 in. thick at second floor, third, and roof levels, respectively. Design live load was: 250 psf for the second floor; 150 psf for the third floor; and 134 psf for the roof (including a sloped cinder fill). There were no girders except for spandrels at the wall line. Columns were 22 in. square at the first story, 18 in. at the second, and 14 in. at the third. All columns had rectangular flared heads, 18 in. deep and extending 20 in. beyond the perimeter of the columns. Concrete was placed as follows: the second floor on October 23-24; the third floor November 11-14; and the roof concrete on December 2 and 3. Supports were removed from beneath the second floor about November 15, leaving one post per panel as continuing support. At the time of the accident forms and centering for the third floor and roof were still in place.[67]

More than half of the third floor had been concreted in balmy weather (51 to 73 F) November 11, but that night the temperature fell to 14 F, remaining cold all the next day (Sunday). On Monday the 13th, the temperature ranged from 12 to 28 F (third floor concrete completed the 14th), and from that day until the date of failure the temperature was below freezing every night except one. There is no record of any protection against the cold, although the sharp drop was predicted and warnings issued by the weather bureau. At these temperatures, there was little or no opportunity for the roof and half of the third floor to develop any strength; all of this weight, plus a possible overload of cinder roof fill, was transmitted through the shoring to the almost entirely unshored second floor.

One theory of failure is that the second floor was seriously overstressed (although it was probably carrying less than its design load) and collapsed. Another possibility is that a failure in the falsework supporting third floor or roof initiated the collapse. Shores were not braced diagonally, and the system (Figure 4.1) for supporting 2x10 beams on the 4x4 shores was relatively unstable. Accidental shaking or disturbance of these posts might

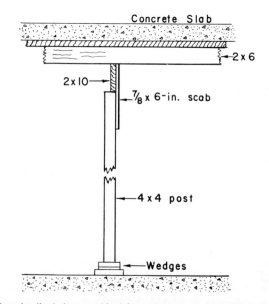

Figure 4.1—One detail of the unstable falsework of the Prestolite Building. Note 2x10 on edge scabbed to one side of the 4x4, creating an eccentric load on shore.

easily have knocked some of the beams off their supports. With only minimal 1x6 horizontal bracing of the shores such a failure could easily become progressive. Absence of cold weather protection was also blamed, because adequate strength development of the third floor and roof could have prevented overloading of the second floor or could have minimized the effect of any shifting or failure in the formwork.

Numerous criticisms and rebuttals were made regarding the structural design. The designer insisted that concrete at the second floor level was defective, testing only 1600 psi at 55 days. The few reshores that had been placed were of doubtful value, and he thought shoring had been knocked out of place (intentionally or otherwise) above the second floor.[68]

Rushed construction schedule, overloaded flat slab with shoring removed too early, lack of cold weather protection for concrete, poor quality sand—these were some of the conditions contributing to the failure of the John Evans Hotel.

JOHN EVANS HOTEL, EVANSTON, ILLINOIS—1925[69]

Twelve bays of four floors and roof of the John Evans Hotel in Evanston, Ill., collapsed at 2:30 P.M., Nov. 3, 1925, when forms were removed from beneath the first floor. The fallen area was about 55x75 ft at the southwest corner of the U-shaped building. Work had progressed rapidly, with no exact records of placement; the contractor-owner estimated the first floor had been in place 20–28 days. There was no record of temperature within the structure, but at a nearby Coast Guard station the temperature records showed an average temperature of 41 F for the 25 days preceding the collapse, with minimum daily temperatures at or below freezing for about half of that time. The owner stated that concrete was protected in the upper floors by canvas and with salamanders for a few days after each section was placed, but no such protection is visible in photographs taken immediately after the wreck.

The first floor was a flat slab with four-way reinforcement, 8½ in. thick, designed for 100 psf live load. The upper three floors and roof were of concrete joist construction (2 in. of concrete over the pan forms), with straight rodded columns spaced about 20 ft on centers both ways. Upper floors were designed for 40 psf live load, and with their forms weighed about 60 psf. This would have placed a 240 psf load on the first floor when it was unshored, assuming that the upper floors had not become self-supporting. Even if they had hardened enough to carry part of their own weight, there would still have been considerable excess over the 100 psf for which the first floor was designed.

Sand from the excavation had been used for all of the structure except the part that failed. For the failed portion, sand obtained from a local building supply dealer had 8 to 10 percent clay and silt. No compression test cylinders or checks on the actual strength of concrete were made, and superficial examination indicated the concrete was "not very good." Since there was no loss of life, and since the contractor also owned and was responsible for design of the structure there was no litigation. The contractor attributed it all to "too early removal of the forms."

The two preceding cases both involved a problem which is still significant in today's construction—the danger of overloading a slab designed for rather light live loads with the accumulated weight of multistory construction above it. Adequate reshoring must be provided for such slabs, and to plan sufficient reshoring the builder should consider the slab's design load as well as its curing history.

FIELD INSPECTION AND SUPERVISION

Competent and strict, almost unfriendly, supervision seems to be one key to the problem of how to prevent failures. In many of the cases described in this monograph there are instances of errors in performance which could have been prevented by proper supervision of the work.

Some 30 years ago, the author designed a three-tier concrete home where concreting was specified to follow inspection and approval of reinforcement in place. At the arranged date for an inspection, the slab bars were all in place but the beam bars had not yet arrived at the job. On the next day, without appointment, the inspection trip was repeated, only to find the concrete already completed and a truckload of beam bars just arrived. It took considerable argument to have a strip of beam bottom form removed and the still-soft concrete chopped out to see the beam bars. They were all ⅜ in. and the contractor had merely substituted two ⅜-in. bars for each ¾-in. or larger bar required. Only after a threat of calling the police was followed by an actual trip toward the station, did the contractor agree to immediately demolish the floor and rebuild it.

Another case is that of a group of garden apartment houses founded on wood piles. A small percentage of the walls almost immediately after completion showed serious distress and settlement cracks. Considerable time and money were spent on new borings and soil studies. Piles exposed and jacked showed completely satisfactory resistance. Exposure of the concrete grade beam immediately gave the explanation. The tops of some pile caps had been installed below plan elevations and the grade beam built exactly as per plan resting on a layer of backfill *above* the pile cap.

Failure was forestalled by inspection in another incident some years ago. The footing for a cantilever-type retaining wall had already been built, when it was noticed that the dowels for the stem were being bent out of position and the reinforcement for the wall itself was being placed along the front or exposed face. A routine inspection stopped the work. The foreman in charge, an old, experienced concrete worker, insisted that the plan was wrong and he was making a "fix." As he argued, the cantilever wall had two faces; the back face was held by the earth fill, but the front face also needed support, and that was where he was placing the bars. He was replaced.

One of a series of failures which brought on the editorial warning quoted in Chapter 2 (p. 12) was the collapse of a three-story department store in Corning, N.Y., described below.

WING AND BOSTWICK DEPARTMENT STORE, CORNING, NEW YORK—1903[70, 71]

This three-story building was 90 ft long, 53 ft wide at the front, and 62 ft at the rear. Floors and walls of the five-bay structure were of concrete, with steel wire-mesh reinforcement in the slabs. Construction was virtually complete, but the structure had not yet been occupied. Specifications contained a clause requiring load testing in the presence of the architect before acceptance of the structure—a load of 400 psf on the first floor and 200 psf on the upper stories, to be applied in at least two 5x5-ft areas of each floor. If there were excessive deflection, the contractor would be required to replace the construction at his own expense.

The first floor had been tested and found satisfactory according to the specifications; the upper floors had not yet been tested, and the architects complained that rumors had reached them that there was insufficient reinforcement in the slabs. On Dec. 15, 1903, two rear bays of the roof and the rear bay of all three floors, including the rear wall, collapsed under dead load only (Figure 4.2). Most of the columns in the collapse area remained standing.

Inspection of the wreckage confirmed the architects' complaint that reinforcement had been omitted at several points. The amount of reinforcing fabric exposed after the failure indicated poor bonding of concrete to steel, but the architect deemed "the failure entirely attributable to the fact that reinforcement of the concrete in that part which failed was almost entirely omitted."

Calling this an object lesson in concrete-steel work, *Engineering News*[71] commented, "It emphasizes the fact, already well known to engineers as well as contractors, that concreting, to be satisfactory,

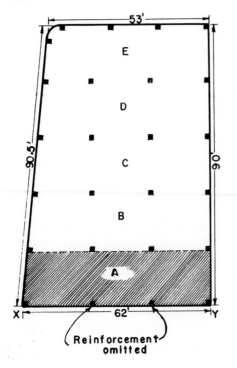

Figure 4.2—Collapse area of Wing and Botswick Department Store included two rear bays (A and B) of the roof and rear bay of all three floors. Most of the rear wall, X-Y, gave way. Columns in the collapse area remained standing, except for those between Sections A and B at the third-floor level.

must be constructed under constant, thorough, and conscientious supervision to ensure that materials, mixture, and placing come up to the standard at all points."

The following failure, which occurred before the structure was occupied, cost four lives and seven injuries, when the building collapsed on a frame dwelling next door. Findings of an investigating committee squarely placed responsibility for failure on the inadequate inspection and supervision, although numerous other deficiencies in the project were cited.

Henke Building, Cleveland, Ohio—1910[72-78]

The 90x103-ft building replaced an earlier structure of the same size, destroyed by fire. Drawings were made for a wall-bearing building of mill construction, but alternate bids were taken on brick walls (using part of the old structure) plus reinforced concrete columns, girders, and rib and tile floor, with the slab cast monolithic with the girders. There were no plans for a concrete structure at the time contract was signed, but the successful bidder agreed to furnish a design. From the beginning, haste was evident. The contract called for 90-day delivery date, with the building structure, four stories and basement, to be completed November 10.

The first floor was designed for 125 psf live load, and other floors were to carry 100 psf live load. Tiles were 8x8x12 in., with 4-in. ribs between and 2-in. topping on floors, 1 in. on the roof slab.

The building was practically complete when, with considerable warning noise, almost the entire structure collapsed in about one minute on the evening of Nov. 22, 1910. Fatalities occurred in an adjoining residence when the Henke Building walls were thrown over on the frame structure. Concreting of the roof had been completed about November 10, and shoring supporting the roof was still in place on the fourth floor when collapse came. A few 4x4 shores remained in place on the third floor. No shores had been removed for the last four days before the collapse.

Initial failure was believed to have occurred in the east section of the fourth floor, or the third story columns, or both. The roof fell almost straight and undisturbed so that it covered its original position, and several floors were found stacked one on top of the other at the northeast corner of the building. Part of the old brick walls which had survived the original fire were left standing, as were most of the columns to heights varying from the first to third floor level. Most of the floor reinforcement had pulled out of the standing colunms.

Approximate age of the concrete at time of collapse was:

2nd floor	70 days
3rd floor	43 days
4th floor	28–35 days
roof	12 days

Roof concrete was still soft when examined the day after the failure. Concrete of the fourth floor had fractured along the surface of aggregate particles. Unfavorable weather conditions existed during the construction of third and fourth story columns, the fourth floor, and the roof. From October 22 to November 22 there were 16 days with the temperature below 32 F, with the low for the period being 25 F. Sand for the concrete was unwashed, excavated from the cellar of the building; it had been removed from near the column footings. Investigators expressed the opinion that there was no settlement of these footings, but did not report actual measurements.

After exhaustive study,* a six-man investigating committee indicated that premature removal of forms and supports in the third story was the immediate cause of failure, but charged the architects, contractor, owner, and Cleveland Department of Buildings with negligence as follows:

> The architects were found negligent for their failure to provide or insist on proper inspection; they also failed to give adequate consideration to time of form removal in cold weather, and failed to advise the owner of the rapidity with which work could be properly executed.

> The contractor was negligent: (1) in providing poor, ignorant, and inexperienced workers; (2) careless placing of reinforcing steel; (3) erecting concrete members of insufficient size and poor quality, containing sawdust, bad sand, and insufficient cement (20 percent less was delivered to the job than required); and (4) removing forms without the architect's consent before the concrete was sufficiently strong.

> The owner was negligent in failing to employ a special inspector as advised by the architects.

> The Department of Buildings was negligent in failing to inspect and insist on compliance with the existing city code.

Having found so much at fault in construction of the Henke Building, the commission apparently did not give much consideration to possible defects of the design. Both Edward Godfrey[75] and C. A. P. Turner[77] charged publicly that there were serious design flaws.

In the next case described, collapse fortunately took place before any live load was applied. Reportedly there was *no inspector and no supervision by the engineer.*

CONCRETE GIRDER BRIDGE, INDEPENDENCE, OREGON—1916[79,80]

A reinforced concrete girder bridge at Independence, Ore., collapsed Sept. 21, 1916, when the bridge forms were stripped. There was no live load. Both columns of one bent settled, and the supported girder of the middle span failed at the point of minimum shear resistance (Figure 4.3).

---

* The investigating commission included representatives from the Cleveland Engineering Society, Cleveland Chapter of the American Institute of Architects, and the local Builders Exchange. These men made nine visits to the ruins, held 17 public sessions, 28 private sessions, attended 5 coroner's sessions, and quizzed almost a hundred witnesses.

After dropping about 4 ft the columns developed sufficient resistance to carry the load, thus preventing total collapse, but leaving a totally useless structure. The broken columns were reinforced with four ¾-in. bars at the corners, plus some wire wrapping. Calculated unit stress under dead load was 200 psi.

Poor concrete was found—at the bottom of the columns there was smooth gravel with mortar not adhered to aggregate, attributed to insufficient mixing as well as clay on the gravel. At the immediate point of failure there were large pockets of coarse aggregate with little sand in the mortar, caused either by lack of mixing or segregation (or both). A 2x8-board was embedded in one column near the point of failure.

There was no supervision by the designing engineer and no inspector on the job to see that the work was properly conducted. Complete omission of responsible supervision was costly, for repair involved almost total reconstruction of the bridge.

Although the grand jury investigating the following more recent collapse found defects in design, material, and construction, a prime lesson to be drawn was contained in the jury's emphasis on the need for "over-all engineering or professional supervision and inspection." Later investigation by the author revealed foundation defects which initiated the collapse—defects which were overlooked for want of competent supervision.

FLAT PLATE OFFICE BUILDING, SCARSDALE, NEW YORK—1953[81-83]

Three men died and ten were injured when the corner of a four-story reinforced concrete office building in Scarsdale, N.Y., collapsed. Failure came at 6:10 P.M., July 10, 1953, as the men were working overtime to complete concrete placement on the fourth floor of the flat plate structure. A coroner's jury was not able to determine the proximate cause of the collapse, nor did it make any charges of criminal negligence, but it did express the opinion that "there existed in said structure at the time of the collapse certain defects in design, material, and construction which may have caused or contributed to the collapse."

Consulting engineers who investigated for the Scarsdale Village Board reported that low-strength concrete, missing or misplaced steel, exterior columns weak in bending, and inadequate reshoring may all have contributed to the disaster. Cores taken from the completed slabs showed significantly different strength test results from those reported for cylinders cast at the time of placement; in some cases concrete tested below the design stresses for the members. Cracks found in exterior columns suggested probable overstress there as well.

Noting that some reinforcing steel was omitted from shop drawings for some slabs, the investigators sought and found cracks in corresponding areas of the slabs as built. There were also deep cracks extending across several floor panels at about one-quarter the distance between columns. Opening up some of these cracks, top steel was found placed too low or omitted entirely. When widths of slab from 7 to 22 in. were cut away near the cracks, a number of areas were found where there was *no reinforcement,* top or bottom.

The author also found other reasons for overstress in this structure. From personal observation and photographs, a characteristic funnel shape pattern in the debris was noted, with the funnel axis pointing toward one column. Later investigation, after removal of debris, showed this column in the bottom story was tipped toward the exterior wall, and the foundation conditions under the exterior wall columns were not the sound rock called for on the plans. Transfer of load caused overstress and tipping of the interior column, and when this support became inoperative, the slab, unable to span 54 ft, collapsed. Weaknesses cited by other investigators no doubt were contributing factors.

Although working without these data on foundation conditions, the coroner's jury correctly concluded that defects on this job "could have been averted by more adequate over-all engineering or professional supervision and inspection." Certainly the lack of control and inspection of the foundation work cost everyone concerned tremendous sums of money, not to mention injuries and loss of life. The building was almost completely demolished before reconstruction, and some 40 column footings were underpinned or enlarged.

The jury also criticized the local building code as totally inadequate and suggested a modernization or the adoption of the New York State Building

Figure 4.3—This collapse occurred when forms were stripped from a newly built bridge in Independence, Oregon. There was no inspector and no engineering supervision on the job, and careless work prevailed.

Code. The local building code, they thought, should fix responsibility for construction supervision in the hands of a registered engineer-architect, preferably the designer of the structure.

How Can Competent Supervision Be Obtained?

The foregoing cases are but a few of the more dramatic examples of what may happen to concrete construction when inspection is inadequate, or in some cases completely lacking. In various investigations of structural distress, the author has found similar sloppy and shoddy work in masonry, steel, and timber as well as in concrete. How can it be prevented without competent supervision—and how can such supervision be obtained?

Warner Howe[84] in 1960 made a plea for complete control of concrete work by the designing engineer, including the preparation of all reinforcement details and all supervision in the field. Admitting the difficulty of an engineer obtaining a sufficient fee for all of the services suggested, he notes a procedure employed successfully by structural engineers in the Memphis area for over 50 years. There the structural consultant not only receives his design fee from the architect or owner, but also furnishes the concrete and reinforcement shop drawings and detailed supervision of the work as a part of the contractor's construction cost. Possible conflict of interest as well as the restrictions in many professional codes of ethics will probably not permit ready acceptance of such a formula.

Reliance by many owners on supervision control by the municipal building inspectors, usually on the argument that such service has been paid for by the building permit fee, is of questionable value. In some jurisdictions the field supervision is competent and thorough, but in many areas, it is nonexistent, even to the extent (an actual occurrence) of disregarding the fact that an additional story had been built with no change in the approved plans.

Design engineers responded favorably to a plea voiced by *Engineering News-Record*[85] for improved and increased supervision as a means of avoiding collapses. The editorial commented that there ". . . appear to be too many cases of failures of projects where designers are not inspecting the field work. Field inspection is the designer's responsibility. Experience has shown that shirking this responsibility may lead to a tarnished reputation, whether deserved or not. It has been said before, but it is advice worth repeating. Don't take a design contract if it doesn't also include the field supervision." The question of fees could be easily solved if all engineers were to agree on this principle.

Recent decisions of the courts may force acceptance of the principle that there can be no separation of design and supervision.

As an alternate and possibly more palatable form of getting the necessary funds from the project budget, the idea of an over-all insurance program described more fully in Chapter 8 should be explored. Such a system, which has operated successfully in Europe for a number of years, makes use of a technical control bureau which checks all designs before any work is done, then checks construction to see that it proceeds in accordance with design and specifications. Linking such a privately financed control bureau with the insurance for the job would provide financial incentive for eliminating any built-in design weakness as well as halting shoddy or incorrect field practices.

MIXING AND PLACING PROBLEMS

Good concrete cannot result from the placing of a poor mix, nor can a good mix badly placed result in the best quality concrete structure. Concrete technology has greatly advanced from the days when such headlines as "worthless concrete responsible for failure at Cleveland filter plant" appeared in 1916.[86] With accumulated knowledge such as that summarized in ACI standards for proportioning concrete, and for measuring, mixing, and placing, as well as in ASTM standards for materials testing, it is now possible to purchase concrete according to specified strength, with entrained air for extra durability if desired, and with additives to retard or accelerate set and enhance workability of the mix. Mechanical vibration and improved techniques in forming have reduced many of the placing problems and yet, as the following discussion indicates, there are many hurdles remaining before "perfect" concrete can be obtained.

Control of the Concrete Mix

Where an industry is proud of the quality of its product, below-standard batches are thrown away. In breweries, for example, vats which show improper fermentation are connected to the drain and wasted. With concrete the problems are a little different; once the mix is in the forms, it is difficult if not impossible to throw it away.

The widespread use of compression test cylinders as a measure of concrete strength is a great advance over earlier lack of control but still leaves room for improvement. Even though early strength results can be used to predict 28-day strength, the concrete has already hardened in the form before any test results are available. In an attempt to get control checks of concrete before using it, a supplementary system was instituted during construction of the New York Coliseum. Cylinders were made in the field from concrete as delivered before it was deposited in the hopper, and cylinders were weighed immediately. Low weight cylinders caused question as to the suitability of the concrete, which was specified to be made with traprock aggregate. Several cases of the wrong aggregate as well as over-wet mixes were caught this way. Of course this system only supplemented and did not replace the standard compression tests.

If such a method had been used at a repair shop contract at a New Hampshire air base, prolonged discussion and expensive reconstruction of the sill for hanger doors would have been avoided.

Concrete for the air base repairs was under extremely careful control and test. The mix contained Type I cement and a field-added air-entraining agent, but during the period of cement shortages in July, 1955, a carload of Type IA was brought in and used. The result was a concrete with a density of 135 lb per cu ft and a strength of less than 2100 psi at 28 days. The specifications called for 3000 psi and some 20,000 cu yd of concrete had been produced and tested satisfactorily. The low strength concrete came near the end of the job and was delivered on two separate days covering 170 cu yd. The error was not discovered until some intricate embedded steel items were encased. Acceptance of the job was delayed for over a year.

Assuming that the use of Type IA cement was accidental and without knowledge of the builder, here is a case of trouble that could have been avoided by weighing the test cylinders at the time of casting. In that way a mix error can be detected very early and the concrete wasted or removed before too much cost is involved.

In the following case, defective strengths were found in spite of conscientious efforts by contractor, subcontractor, and suppliers to meet specifications of the contract.

AMSTERDAM PLAZA, COLUMBIA UNIVERSITY, NEW YORK, N.Y.—1963[87]

Bad concrete halted construction of Amsterdam Plaza, a landscaped bridge over Amsterdam Avenue south of 117th Street which is to connect the main and east campuses of Columbia University. Several core samples from the first 12 of 22 pillars that support the bridge failed to meet 28-day compressive strength requirements, and the piers were demolished by unanimous agreement of architect, engineer, contractor, and owner. Routine tests during mixing and placing of the concrete had shown no deficiencies. The 28-day strength was determined from test cylinders as well as cores from the piers, and several samples were found to be below required strength. Laboratory tests were immediately commenced in an effort to determine the cause of low strength and to establish proportions for a safer mix.

Difficulty in obtaining specified concrete strengths has resulted in the rather strict supervision requirements of the New York City build-

Figure 4.4—Improper placing techniques, together with lack of suitable vibration, caused a void to be left below the window opening in this concrete wall.

ing code. However, without criticism of the agencies providing and controlling such supervision, it is doubtful whether the required concrete is being produced any better or more often than before the controls were required. The division of responsibility has been given as an explanation for this. The cure being followed by some contractors is to purchase "certified concrete," with the seller guaranteeing compliance with concrete specifications. The seller thus accepts responsibility for losses from low strengths. For many years, the New York City highway contracts have had a penalty charge for the shortage in design strength of the pavement base concrete as shown by cores taken just before final acceptance. This method of control reduces the need for supervision, but does not guarantee obtaining the desired strength.

Validity of Cylinder Test Results

In two building operations designed by the author and under construction some 30 miles apart in Texas, at the same time in 1950, the concrete mix proportions were identical. The same brand of cement and aggregates from a single source were used for both jobs, but there were separate mix plants. The 28-day tests were consistently higher at one job. The average difference was more than 500 psi, not explainable from any variation in slump, temperature, or testing procedures.

On the other hand, on two similar New York housing projects, on opposite sides of a main road, with concrete coming from a single plant and the truck routed at the entrance to either project as agreed upon in the field with no prior instruction, *with different testing laboratories,* one project showed not a single cylinder below the required 3000 psi and the other had consistent low tests.

One can only conclude from these examples that concrete test cylinders are not a perfect indication of the concrete, no more than are spot borings a perfect indication of a subsoil area. Further questions are raised by the 1963 report of the New York District Attorney,[88] which said, on the basis of a 30-month investigation, that "careless and negligent disregard of basic safety precautions" had been found in the testing of concrete for building construction in that city. Although no prosecution for criminal responsibility was undertaken, the report indicated that privately operated testing laboratories had falsified reports to the city on the condition of concrete tested. The district attorney recommended licensing of such laboratories and a requirement that architects and builders use only the licensed testers. His report also urged that safety inspectors should be required to certify to the accuracy of their reports to the city.

Placing and Finishing

No matter how good the concrete mix, it may be unserviceable or totally defective if not properly placed (Figure 4.4). Placing problems leading to deterioration or ultimate collapse include those of incorrectly located reinforcement, excessive concentration of reinforcing bars, insufficient consolidation of concrete, badly placed construction or expansion joints, incorrect location or elevation . . . to mention only a few. Occasionally steel location and concentration make it literally impossible to place concrete, as in the case shown in Figure 4.5—the bottom of a 20 in. wide concrete rigid frame which included seven

Figure 4.5—Concentration of reinforcement in the bottom of a 20-in. frame member. The bars were so close that concrete could not pass between.

#9 bars in the bottom layer and six #9 bars in a second layer. Apparently two of the second layer bars slipped down and no concrete could get through the maze of steel.

Another example of this type of invitation to distress or failure is the case of a shallow concrete dome with enough layers of reinforcement to occupy more than the thickness called for if the steel were to be coated with mortar. The over-all steel mat was so dense that, as the contractor stated, "even rain wouldn't go through." The resulting shape of the dome was not satisfactory although the structure was stable. No amount of argument convinced either side that a better job could be done. It may be good policy for a designer upon completing an unusual program to look at it critically and ask, "Is it buildable?"

CONSTRUCTION JOINTS

That a monolithic structure should be a monolithic placement of concrete seems evident. Yet the prevalence of "cold" joints visible in many completed concrete exposures indicates the disregard of this fact. Cold joints do not often cause failures; some technicians even claim that the concrete is self healing in time, but disintegration seems to center about these weak planes. The early cold-joint failure described below occurred in 1901.

CONCRETE ARCH BRIDGE, JACAGUAS RIVER, PUERTO RICO—1901[89]

This three-span bridge was 404 ft long; the arches were placed in three longitudinal sections, the middle one 9 ft wide and the sides 5.5 ft each. Concrete was hand mixed and deposited from wheelbarrows. Specifications called for monolithic arch sections, but because of frequent heavy rains it was necessary to provide some way the work could be stopped on short notice. The contractor suggested laying concrete in two layers, dividing along the neutral plane, and finishing the work at any time against transverse bulkheads. The government engineer agreed to this procedure.

When the arch centering was struck, masses of concrete fell out, and the separation along the neutral plane in the middle section of the center span was found to be complete. Rains had probably weakened the top of the lower lift, and poor mixing made the trouble worse. The north section of the arch was placed monolithically and remained standing.

The arch bridge failure described below occurred after the structure had been in service several years; cracking was at the cold joint location.

ARCH BRIDGE, TACOMA, WASHINGTON—1922[90]

Partial failure of one of three ribs of a reinforced concrete skewed arch bridge in Tacoma, Wash., occurred in the fall of 1922. The bridge was elliptical in cross section, parallel to the direction of the street, and carried a roadway and street car tracks over a railroad (Figure 4.6). It supported fill extending from the abutments to about 6 ft deep at the crown of the arch. A crack developed near the third point of one of the three sections, where there was an emergency or end-of-day's-work joint. The crack was horizontal, not normal to the ellipse, extending entirely across the rib section; it was a more or less regular opening 1 or 2 in. wide. Some vertical bars were wholly or partially fractured across the crack; others were merely deformed.

An investigating committee appointed by the American Association of Engineers found laitance ½ to 1 in. thick along with wood and rubbish at the failure crack. Water had been seeping through the crack for several years, gradually removing laitance and enlarging the crack. The committee attributed failure to "lack of bond due to laitance left in the emergency joint, augmented by the fact that the joint was not made normal to the thrust of the ring." Numerous layers of laitance ½ to 3 in. thick were found elsewhere in the structure; apparently no effort had been made to clean construction joints as the work progressed.

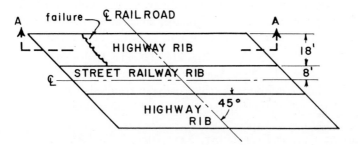

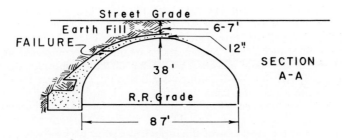

Figure 4.6—This sketch shows plan and elevation of skewed bridge in Tacoma, Washington. Failure plane extended horizontally across one rib at a construction joint.

ESTABLISHING DESIRED SLAB ELEVATION IN BRIDGE WORK

With the attempt to get smooth-riding high speed roadways, and to counterbalance dead load deflections from the concrete deck, steel stringer beams on bridges and viaducts are usually specified to be fabricated with camber. The amount of camber is computed on the basis of assumed rigidity (or merely pin-connection) of the end supports. Unfortunately, the assumptions are often in error. Where end connections are welded, as was found to be the case in a recent investigation of an important New York City viaduct, the dead load deflection from the weight of the concrete slab is far less than computed. If the slab forms are shored, instead of being carried on hangers from the stringers, the total dead load is first carried by a composite section (steel beam plus concrete slab), and practically none of the camber goes out. With the necessary careful inspection, especially with public funds involved, the slab thickness is held to the exact dimension of the plans, and the result is a series of domed spans between girders or expansion joints, and bouncing of traffic on the roadway. In the concreting operation of the Tappan Zee bridge roadway, several miles long, the supervising engineer realized this difficulty and some correction was made in the field by special screeding and finishing of the surface.

In 1960, a section of the Brooklyn-Queens Expressway was closed temporarily by the New York State Department of Public Works.[91] Rough-riding conditions on this roadway resulted from camber which did not go out of the bridge stringers as anticipated.

BROOKLYN-QUEENS EXPRESSWAY, NEW YORK, N.Y.—1960

A 1.2-mile westbound section of elevated, six-lane divided highway was ordered closed for resurfacing 6 months after it opened. This portion of the Brooklyn-Queens Expressway did not meet specifications relative to smoothness and riding qualities. The wearing surface was a 3-in. layer of asphaltic concrete placed on the concrete slab, with the layer being made uniformly and exactly 3 in. thick. Transverse steel expansion joints in the concrete deck of the elevated structure were spaced at 60-ft intervals, extending up through the wearing surface. Specifications required the completed asphalt surface to be at the same elevation as the top of these joints. At the rated 50 mph speed, vehicles were continuously bouncing, and it was found that the joints in the westbound lanes were from ¼ to ½ in. lower than the crown elevation midway between joints. Eastbound lanes fared better because the surfacing material was kept to straight lines between the tops of expansion joint "dams" and the thickness of the asphalt varied as necessary to produce this smooth roadway. When asphalt on the westbound lanes had been removed, careful survey of the concrete surface and of the underside of the stringer beams showed that camber built into the beams had not gone out.

DISHED FLOORS

Concrete floor slabs with monolithic finish, especially in long span designs, are seldom constructed to satisfactorily level tolerances. The customary procedure of screeding the concrete from midspan to column lines pulls the denser materials toward the columns, and upon hardening and drying, the surface is dished. Camber built into formwork to compensate for slab deflection* is voided if the slab is screeded to a fixed elevation; rather, screeds should be set to a constant elevation above the deck forms. Where formwork is not cambered, the top surface can be screeded to a slight dome shape to neutralize slab deflection after the supporting forms are removed. Even then, later shrinkage and plastic flow of the finished concrete plus any creep from loading are not compensated for, and some dishing results.

In the New York Coliseum (1955) exhibition levels, most of this trouble was eliminated by a somewhat unusual procedure. To avoid the later application of a wearing course which would provide a hard level surface to take the 300 psf permissible loading including trucking of the exhibits onto the floor, the design required the slabs to be screeded to templates set about ¼ in. above the desired finish level and troweled with rotary machines after seeding the plastic surface with small chips of traprock. After the concrete had hardened for at least 60 days (with floor meanwhile used for all construction operations with no possible damage to the surface since it had not been finished), the top was ground by heavy terrazzo machines to a level surface which proved entirely satisfactory and has remained quite level. The garage floor slab, where a monolithic cement finish was troweled in while the forms were still in place, showed sufficient dishing to require, in 3 years, the addition of small weep holes in the center of some panels for drainage of water accumulation.

Precasting Difficulties

Shrinkage during setting and curing of precast concrete items made in steel forms has been known to pull the flanges and webs apart, since the forms do not give. Precast joists often show fine cracks where the web joins the flanges; however, if they are reinforced with diagonal steel wires or mesh full scale load tests[92] indicate no reduction in strength from such cracking.

Casting of concrete beams must be detailed and executed so that the resulting dimensions fit the desired ones. In casting some long I-

---

* This should not be confused with the camber of relatively long-span "horizontal shoring" which is intended to counteract deflection of the shoring itself, leaving a level form support when full load of fresh concrete is in place.

shaped girders for a bridge in Yonkers in 1958, with spans from 100 to 113 ft, the anchor bolts were all sufficiently out of place to miss the holes in the abutment seats as described on p. 50. The erection schedule was seriously affected by the necessary field welding and anchor adjustment at each beam as it was held in place by two cranes.

The cost of field adjustment, welding, and joint grouting becomes a serious concern when precast units for building assembly are not precisely made. In a large housing development near Chicago in 1952, the labor expended in this corrective and connecting work was almost equal to the labor of making and delivering the castings. Results of economic comparisons can be reversed if the units are not true and square as the designer assumed. Realistic consideration in the design stage should be given to the possibility of producing units to desired shape and dimensional tolerances at the expected cost.

PRECASTING STRESSES

It is not often realized that precast concrete units also have locked-in stresses. Sometimes these stresses result in cracking or distorted shapes after some aging. One serious case was the discovery of cracks in the post-tensioned beams for a tunnel approach viaduct described below.

PRESTRESSED BEAMS, TUNNEL APPROACH VIADUCT, HAMPTON ROADS, VIRGINIA—1958

Standard I-shaped beams, 3 ft deep and up to 86 ft long, were both pre-tensioned and post-tensioned. Pretensioning was done with small diameter wires anchored in the concrete throughout their length. Post-tensioning was by end-anchored parallel wire cables in sheaths which were later grouted. Beams were fabricated in late fall of 1957, and in the winter serious cracks appeared in the webs and soffits of the beams, closely outlining the location of the metal sheaths for the post-tensioned cables. Nearly 100 of the beams were rejected, and the bridge job delayed.

First reports[93] were that the grout had frozen in the beams and opened cracks which later enlarged. But when similar cracks were found in some of the beams cast in May, 1958, to replace the almost 100 rejected ones, another explanation was found necessary. The true cause was found to be the unequal shrinkage of different concrete thicknesses after steam curing. The metal sheaths acted as radiators to cause rapid local cooling, and some fine separation cracks developed. Grouting under pressure, after the post-tensioning was completed, opened the cracks. A number of shorter prestressed stringers built in the same shop, without post-tensioning, showed no cracking. Investigation of other casting plant practice disclosed that similar trouble under like conditions had been experienced and that steam curing had been discontinued in some British plants where metal sheaths or metal forms were used.

HOT AND COLD WEATHER

Optimum temperatures for curing concrete are well known today, and precautions for protecting concrete against extremes of high temperature or frost have been well defined in the ACI standards for hot and cold weather concreting and documented by the research of a number of organizations. Concrete can be safely installed in freezing weather if precautions are taken and frost protection equipment is prepared and available before work is started. Likewise, quality concrete can be produced in very warm weather if proper protective measures are planned. Because these measures may require extra labor and add to the apparent cost of the work, they are sometimes disregarded unless supervision is strict. A contractor may also be the victim of sudden, unseasonable temperature changes, and be inadequately prepared to protect concrete. Early failures due to freezing were common before builders realized the possibility of damage, as some of the cases presented will show. Even today, in spite of all of the knowledge about temperature control and protective measures, there are still some cases of distress and collapse caused by temperature extremes.

Cold Weather—Frozen Concrete

Ignorance and carelessness in winter concreting show up quickly with the arrival of warm weather; frozen concrete may have some strength—and a good appearance—until it thaws out. If its frozen condition is known, very careful provisions for supporting and curing it at higher temperature until it attains strength may save the structure, but alternate freezing and thawing will cause disintegration.

A number of serious failures in the early part of the century were caused largely by ignorance or disregard of proper methods and protection in cold weather. The collapse of Reed's Bath House[94] in Atlantic City in 1906 was attributed to frost penetration of the freshly placed concrete. The one-story structure had brick walls and a concrete slab and girder roof supported on interior columns as well as the bearing wall. Frost penetration of varying depths in the girders was found, and columns were reduced to rubble—the photographed remains looked like a purposely demolished structure. Concrete was of such poor quality that it could be broken off and crushed in the hand. Poor quality brick work and improper placing (roof beams apparently placed to the underside of the slab, with the slab cast separately) made a bad situation even worse.

Frozen concrete was clearly to blame for the partial collapse of the bakery described below; note that the failure occurred nearly three weeks after form removal, at a period of warmer weather.

SCHUST BAKING BUILDING, SAGINAW, MICHIGAN—1915[95]

This five-story building with reinforced concrete floors, frame, and roof was designed to house heavy baking equipment which had not yet been installed. The monitor and part of the roof fell February 11, carrying down that part of the fifth floor directly beneath. Examination of the wreckage indicated that failure had begun with the collapse of a 19-ft column on the fifth floor, which simply disintegrated for a height of about 6 ft at its base.

Appearance of the concrete indicated that it had been frozen. The inspector on the job said that concrete for the fifth floor columns and spandrels had been placed November 13 and 14, and the roof had been concreted about 10 days later. Frost protection was not thought necessary. However, a recheck of local weather records showed daily minimum temperatures below freezing before the placement of columns. Then, temperatures ranged from 32 to 52 F from November 12 to November 15; on the 16th, the temperature went below freezing and remained subfreezing until noon November 18, with a minimum of 15 F. There was no appreciable thaw until November 24.

Forms were removed about mid-January, 1915, and the roof and columns remained unsupported until the failure occurred at 6 P.M., February 11. The temperature from January 16 to February 10 had remained below freezing. At 9 P.M. February 10, the temperature rose above 32 F and remained warmer until after the failure. The building at this time was also heated by steam from the interior.

Cold weather was one of several construction problems in the following incident which was the first recorded reinforced concrete failure in Cincinnati. This case shows the disastrous results of ignorant and over-zealous attempts at economy.

EASTERN AVENUE THEATER, CINCINNATI, OHIO—1912[96]

A proposed theater building, 31x98 ft, was completely wrecked during form removal Dec. 10, 1912. The one-story building had a reinforced concrete floor at street level, supported on a beam-girder-column system on a lot which sloped about 25 ft to the rear (Figure 4.7). The reinforced floor slab was about 5½ in. thick, designed for a live load of 80 psf. A column and footing originally planned between Columns 9 and 10 were omitted because of a trunk sewer at this point. Footings 9 and 10 were enlarged and the girder section changed from 8x30 in. to 12x55 in. to compensate for the omission.

Original drawings and specifications were prepared by an architect and engineer; after the bidding, the owner entered an agreement with a local contractor to revise the design and construct the building for substantially less than the low bid. (It appears that he merely traced the original plans to get a building permit.) The contractor built the forms himself with lumber that he planned to use later for roofing the building; he engaged an inexperienced concrete contractor who completed concreting about November 9 without competent supervision.

Exterior brick walls were then built on the new concrete floor while all the forms remained in place. The next step seems to have been removal of all the forms, except beam and girder bottoms and their supports. This did not provide enough lumber to finish the roof, and the contractor ordered the remainder of the forms removed. No trouble was encountered until the supports were removed from girders framing into Column 9, supporting the 13-in. brick walls about 22 ft high. When these shores were pulled, collapse of the entire structure followed, without sufficient warning for workmen to get out of the building.

This was on December 10, just one month after concreting had been finished. The temperature had dropped considerably below 32 F several days during the month, and curing conditions had not been at all favorable for form removal at this time. This was something which the men on the job utterly failed to understand. There was no doubt that the low temperature resulting in improperly hardened concrete was the immediate cause

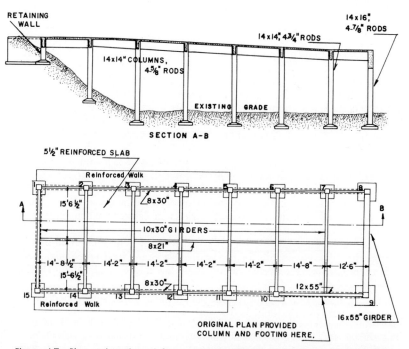

Figure 4.7—Plan and section of floor system for Cincinnati theater which collapsed one month after concreting when shores were removed from girders framing into Column 9. Cold weather problems were aggravated by poor construction practices.

of the failure. However, close inspection of the wreckage showed careless placing of tension steel; many rods were bunched close together leaving little or no room for concrete to flow between.

Probably the most complete failure in the history of concrete construction was the frost damage collapse of seven stories of a proposed eight-story hotel described below. Most of the concrete in the debris could be simply shoveled away; only a few of the lower story columns and first floor beams remained.

HOTEL VINCENT, BENTON HARBOR, MICHIGAN—1924[97, 98]

Construction on the eight-story Hotel Vincent had been started late in November, 1923, and continued until January 28, when placement of the eighth floor was being completed. Shoring was removed the same day beneath the fifth floor, and that night the fifth floor began to fail. By midnight, three central bays of this floor had collapsed on the west side; by morning these same three bays were collapsed from the eighth floor to the ground, leaving a great gash down the face of the structure. Collapse continued gradually throughout the day, as the structure "melted" away. By the morning of January 30 the entire building was a heap of rubble, except for a small two-story portion in the rear.

Investigators found no fault with the structural design.* Materials for the concrete were also found satisfactory, when tested after the disaster. Although some evidence suggested the concrete mix was leaner than specified, almost total responsibility for the collapse rested on the low temperatures at the time of concreting, together with the insufficient protection provided against frost damage. A recording thermometer about three blocks away from the hotel showed the daily minimum temperature throughout November, December, and January was below 40 F except for two days. During January, minimum daily temperature, except for one day, was consistently below 30 F. The fifth floor where failure began was concreted December 28 and 29, when the minimum temperature was 24 F. This was followed by two severe cold waves, with low temperatures of 2 F and −16 F. Fifth-story columns and sixth floor were concreted during the extreme cold, and the temperature did not rise above freezing again until January 6. Sixth-story columns, the seventh floor, seventh-story columns, and the eighth floor were all placed during subsequent periods in January when temperatures did not rise above freezing.

Tarpaulins were available for only one story of construction, and only 16 salamanders were available for the entire job. Some heating of mixing water and aggregates was reported, along with the addition of calcium chloride

---

* The building was 100x100 ft. in plan, with a 56 ft. square portion at the rear corner only two stories high. The rest of the structure was to be eight stories, with square columns connected by deep longitudinal girders in each of the two long dimensions. The floor was of concrete joist construction—a slab 2 in. thick with joists 6 in. deep and 5 in. wide spaced 25 in. on centers. These joists spanned about 14 ft. between girders. Interior columns were spirally reinforced, and face columns had longitudinal steel tied at 12-in. intervals.

to the mix, but no record of mix temperature was kept. The temperature precautions were clearly insufficient . . . three or four days protection was the maximum that any one story received. "Due to the almost complete breaking up of the concrete, it was difficult to find pieces large enough for compression tests."[98] Five samples taken from the debris tested from 247 to 718 psi.

Cold-weather failures like those portrayed in the foregoing cases are isolated instances today rather than being almost commonplace as they were years ago. Racey[99] in 1957 described a more recent case, indicating that frost failures do still occur in spite of advances in knowledge. Footings for a four-story structure were cast on frozen ground. The concrete froze before it could set, and the footings remained frozen for an extended period while foundation walls were being concreted. Work was at the superstructure level by the time warm spring weather arrived. As temperatures rose, the ground under some of the footings thawed and the footings began to disintegrate. Settlement followed, resulting in serious damage and near collapse of a large part of the structure. Part of the structure had to be dismantled and rebuilt.

Even where nominal frost protection is provided, contact of freshly placed concrete with existing structures at low temperatures may cause trouble, as in the following case of the Erie Railroad crossing of the Chemung River in New York.

Circular columns about 3 ft in diameter were concreted in midwinter, resting on pile caps about 6x30x5 ft. The columns were given moderate protection with tarpaulins and salamanders, but when the forms were removed the bottom 3 ft of concrete was marble-white. The great mass of pile cap at below-zero temperature had simply frozen the bottom few feet of the shaft in spite of heated materials and a heated enclosure.

Many smaller scale structures are vulnerable to this same type of problem.

In spite of improved understanding of the need for cold weather protection, superstructures still occasionally suffer damage, as the unfortunate progress of winter concreting on an unidentified building in the Montreal area demostrates.[99, 100]

The structure was a three-story reinforced concrete building about 200x85 ft, with columns spaced about 20 ft on centers. Construction proceeded normally during the fall, and the roof slab was placed December 11 and 12. Tarpaulins were hung around the upper story, but no real provision was made for protecting the freshly placed concrete from freezing. Without heat the tarpaulins were useless, because the concrete sections were thin and exposed. On the night of December 12, outside temperature dropped to 10 F, and the air within the tarpaulins went to the same level.

Figure 4.8—Collapse of frost-damaged roof of Montreal building during January thaw occurred about 10 minutes after the last man climbed down from the masons' scaffold (still in place at lower right).

Later in December, there was a thaw while forms and shores were still in place. About a month later (January 10) forms and shores supporting the roof slab were removed when the temperature was well below freezing. The building remained unshored, and bricklaying was started on January 24 along the south wall. The next morning it started to rain and the bricklayers were laid off. About 10 minutes after the last man climbed down from the scaffold, the whole south portion of the roof slab collapsed (Figures 4.8 and 4.9). Apparently the earlier thaw did not last long enough to allow the concrete to defrost and cure sufficiently to support itself in the unfrozen state.

Not only was the direct loss of a substantial portion of this structure serious in itself; physical removal of the collapsed section was hazardous to the workmen in the salvage crew and to the rest of the structure. Adjacent outside roof panels along the fallen section had to be removed as well as the supporting columns. The lesson learned from this failure cost the contractor a very large amount—bankruptcy.

Laxness in cleaning ice and snow from forms also may cause serious difficulties. Ice or hard-packed snow will not necessarily be melted when the warm concrete is placed on top of it (Figure 4.10). Dangerous voids as well as frozen concrete may be the result.

Danger to precast beams after post-tensioning, from the freezing of the grout while sealing the cable sheaths, has been reported at a number of locations. One recommended procedure to avoid this damage (coming from Scandinavian sources) is to mix alcohol into the grout to act as an antifreeze. The expansive force of frozen grout acting across unreinforced faces of concrete will completely shatter the highly compressed casting.

The dangers to concrete work in freezing weather are well documented. Today the necessary frost protection measures are known,[101] but this knowledge is of no use if the needed equipment is not assembled and made available before frost strikes. After concrete is frozen, no frost protection methods will cure the trouble—the concrete must not be permitted to thaw partly and refreeze. Any concrete program in the winter where frost is a possibility must be preceded by a complete assembly of all wind breaks, heating devices and distribution necessary to protect against the coldest day for the largest expected area of work. Only such insurance will protect against weather damage to the work.

Hot Weather

When concreting is undertaken in hot weather without any special precautions, any or all of the following effects may be experienced:[102]

1. Setting is accelerated, shortening the time available for proper placement and finishing.
2. Strength is reduced because of effects on the hydration process.
3. The tendency toward cracking, either before or after hardening, is increased.
4. Adequate curing becomes a more critical requirement.
5. Control of air content in air-entrained concrete is made more difficult.

While these difficulties do not often lead to serious collapse or other evident failures, they do contribute to general lowering of the quality of concrete produced. If the strength goes far below the level specified, this alone may be a "failure" sufficient to cause rejection of the finshed work.

Hot weather was blamed for the under-strength concrete on a dormitory, pharmacy building, and a $3.7-million coliseum in Athens, Georgia, in 1962. An engineering investigation was undertaken.[103]

HANDLING AND ERECTION DIFFICULTIES

Moving or lifting of a prefabricated structural unit—whether a precast pile, the suspended span of a cantilever bridge, a precast, prestressed or plain reinforced beam or a lift slab section—can only be

Figure 4.9—Closeup view of Montreal roof slab shows column and drop panel still standing, surrounded by failed slab sections. Note how reinforcement pulled out of frost-weakened concrete.

safely accomplished if erection stresses do not go beyond the yield points, and if the lifting equipment provides sufficient continuous and uniform supports. Failures in this class frequently result from insufficiency of small details or nonuniform action of the lifting hardware. Another common cause is the absence of adequate bracing during erection and assembly. Small horizontal forces will upset the neutral equilibrium existing during the upward lifting of a large mass if it is laterally unrestrained.

Horizontal loading during erection—wind on one side of an almost completed job—caused the failure of a 5-million-gal. tank at Littleton, Colorado. The 100 ft diameter water storage tank was made of vertical precast staves, 6x28 ft, set with edges tight. After more than half the height had been wrapped with die-stressed wires and completely grouted, six staves fell inward, releasing all wire tension, and all the wires had to be removed. While the discussion of responsibility was going on, a similar tank with all staves in position also collapsed from lateral wind pressure before any wire had been installed.

Handling problems may be especially critical for prestressed members as an incident at Wellington, New Zealand, in 1955 demonstrates.[104] During transfer of 105-ft. prestressed beams from casting bed to stockpile, one of the trucks ran into a depression; a beam tipped over and exploded from the release of the prestress as it deflected laterally. The shock set off a beam standing vertically, and that also broke into fragments. Failure of a long prestressed girder being hauled through Providence, R.I., in 1962 was caused by sidesway as the truck made a curve. The beam broke in half from lack of lateral resistance for its dead load alone.

The lightweight precast 80-ft T's for a school gymnasium roof in Arizona were shipped 300 miles to the job site, and it is suspected that this long haul may have significantly reduced the bond of the pretensioned strands. Although the T-members were lifted from casting bed, placed on the trailer, and erected on the walls without incident, the beams developed an early sag of 6 to 8 in. When a heavy rainfall caused further deflection, the roof was rejected. The combination of dynamic loading during transportation with the lower bond strength developed in lightweight concrete seems to be the reasonable explanation.

For hoisting precast members, spreaders or lifting beams which will insure vertical application of loads at the correct points should always be used. The designer should provide additional reinforcement for any reversed stresses that will occur during erection.

Lack of adequate bracing to resist lateral forces is a continuing source of accidents and collapses during construction, so much so that numerous warnings have been issued and code provisions like the following British one have been adopted:[105]

> All practicable precautions shall be taken by the use of temporary guys, stays, supports and fixings or otherwise where necessary to prevent danger to any person employed through the collapse of any part of a building or other structure during any temporary state of weakness or instability of the building or structure or part thereof before the structure is completed.

This regulation is designed to protect the construction worker, but its proper implementation would protect the construction work as well. The designing engineer or architect can contribute to such a goal by considering methods of erection and carrying out the work at every

Figure 4.10—Accumulated ice and snow must be removed from forms before concreting. Here the contractor discovered that the hard packed snow did not melt but became a part of the concrete beam above these windows.

stage of the design, instead of leaving them wholly to the contractor.

Failure during erection of part of the precast framing of the warehouse at Harrisonburg, Va., in 1961 (described on p. 34) was attributed by some to faulty bearing details. However, investigation brought out a number of questionable erection practices which may have contributed to the failure.

A British journal[105] has reported several cases of precast concrete beams of symmetrical section which had not been marked in any way to show which was the top and which the bottom. Of course the main reinforcement was provided in only one place. Sooner or later a beam of this type is placed on its supports upside down, and then it is only a matter of time until failure occurs. It was with this problem in mind that an American engineer specified that the word "top" be marked on top of each unit of an order of 100-ft girders. However, the girders were delivered upside down, and the marking was concealed against the bed of the truck. A little more foresight would have put "bottom" on the bottom as well.

Lift Slab Work

Wide acceptance of the recently developed technique known as "lift slab" has been delayed somewhat by several erection failures. There were three successive failures on three separate attempts to complete a 175,000-lb lift slab roof section at Ojus, Florida, in 1952 (see p. 28). Only the last was attributed to any structural design deficiency. The first failure was in a 5-in. pipe stub supporting a jack on top of the permanent column; the pipe buckled and dropped the jack while eccentricity in lifting was being adjusted. The second failure was triggered by stripping of defective threads on the inverted flange supporting the slab. The third failure was a shearing in the edge of the concrete cap above the column (computed unit shear was 93 psi over the circular concrete section).

A live load of interested spectators compounded problems (and subsequent damage suits) during erection of the first lift slab in the San Francisco Bay area.

SERRA HIGH SCHOOL LIFT SLAB ROOF, SAN MATEO, CALIFORNIA—1954

A 60x70-ft roof slab for a shop building of the Serra High School fell when near its full 16-ft height. The 8½-in. slab was being lifted on nine 6-in. pipe columns. Each column was attached to its footings by four anchor bolts of ½-in. and ¾-in. size. Observers noted that the columns were 3 in. out of plumb to the east, and while the guys were being adjusted to counteract this leaning, the slab drifted laterally and fell about 15 ft west of its original position. Eight men standing on the slab were injured.

One investigator listed the following reasons for the failure: [107]

1. Design would not permit lateral loading without bracing during lifting, and two directional bracing had not been provided.

2. Added live load of spectators may have created irregular column stresses when the observers were concentrated on one side of the slab.

3. Lateral shifting of the slab created an eccentric load that caused column failure.

Four injured spectators were awarded more than $100,000 damages as the result of litigation in a California court. [108] The verdict was against the architect, general contractor, and lift-slab contractor. Fortunately most of the observers had been cleared from the slab before it fell.

A wind storm with possible gusts of 35 to 50 mph—normal late spring weather in Cleveland—was blamed for shifting the next described lift slab structure out of position.

LIFT SLAB GARAGE, CLEVELAND, OHIO—1956 [109, 110]

Eight-story twin towers, each 91x21 ft in plan, were being erected by the lift slab method, with the 8-in. slabs weighing 180,000 lb each concreted at ground level and raised by jacks atop the steel columns. Floor slabs in each section were supported on 61 ft high columns spaced about

Figure 4.11—Winds of 35-50 mph acting against unfinished slab-to-column connections were blamed for shifting this 8-story lift slab structure about 6.5 deg out of plumb. The building was successfully righted by jacking diagonally between columns.

22 ft on centers. Columns were hollow, made of two welded steel angles and were to be filled later with concrete. Cast steel collars were embedded in each slab around the column openings, for purpose of lifting and later anchorage to the columns.

All eight tiers of the west tower had been raised into position by the close of work on April 6, and were held in place by temporary steel wedges. The erector planned to weld all connections at one time instead of welding collars to columns floor by floor as each slab reached its final position. During the night, the winds came, varying from 10 mph upward to gusts of 35–50 mph. The structure shifted in the direction of its long dimension, and the top came to rest nearly 7 ft out of plumb (Figure 4.11). The fifth floor was within inches of an existing lower building. The east tower had the second and third floors in place, with the rest of the slabs held temporarily within the next two stories, and was not affected by the wind.

Guys were attached to the framing early April 7, but the structure appeared to be stable without tightening the guys. Temporary shoring was installed on order of the Cleveland building commissioner, who remarked[109] that "if they had welded at each floor as they went along the building would have been braced and this would not have happened."

The designer asserted that computed stresses for the deflected steel columns were below the plastic range for structural steel. Within about a month, the contractor began jacking diagonally between the top and bottom of successive columns[110] to right the structure. The complete success of the restoration operation speaks well of the original design, but a little care in the erection program would have easily avoided this trouble.

SEPARATION OF SLABS

There have been some problems of improper separation where lift slabs are cast on completed concrete. In a building at Utica, N.Y., in 1956, separation was forced by eccentric jacking and large areas of the ceiling were ripped off, exposing the reinforcement and requiring expensive repair. Similar difficulty in a lift slab operation in eastern Pennsylvania was corrected by drilling through the top slab and jarring the contact surface with black powder. The experience of local coal miners was used to good advantage. In 1960 at Salisbury, Md., a roof slab lift took with it the finished mesh-reinforced grade floor slab, nearly 8000 sq ft. After unsuccessful attempts to pry the slab loose, small holes were drilled on a 1x1½-ft grid and 3500 charges of 1 oz of 40 percent gelatin were shot off four holes at a time, to demolish the unwanted floor slab attached to the ceiling. The great number of successful separations in lift slab operations indicates that proper care in the spreading of a good bond prevention medium would eliminate such difficulties.

5

Construction Problems:
Formwork Failures

FORMWORK FAILURES and failures caused by improper reshoring or premature removal of formwork supports have been all too common, throughout the history of concrete construction. Of course, when a building collapses during construction it is easy to blame the formwork, since it and much of the other evidence are covered by the wreckage. Such an explanation sometimes conveniently masks the real cause of trouble, but formwork has truly been at fault in so many cases that it must bear strong scrutiny in any treatment of failures.

Formwork today is seldom too weak to carry the direct vertical load of freshly placed concrete, but all too often it lacks sufficient bracing to withstand the various lateral loads that may be imposed during construction. Lateral forces may be set up by the starting and stopping of rapidly moving buggies or by dumping loads of fresh concrete on the deck. Heavy piles of construction material, nonsymmetrical placement of concrete, and wind create unbalanced forces which call for bracing.

Premature removal of forms and shores and careless practices in reshoring have caused numerous failures, or defects such as sagging or cracking in the completed structure. Inadequate size or spacing of reshores may bring the danger of collapse during construction. Defective mudsills or other base supports for formwork are also responsible for failures.

Interestingly, the same form design, or even the same form itself, may have been used several times previous to failure with no mishap.

Few failures are reported at the beginning of jobs, seldom in small operations. There is frequently a common pattern—a fast rate of placing the concrete at a stage in construction where the forms have been used several times and the work is routine. At times, this is just a matter of luck giving out. Perhaps the formwork is not well braced, but fortunately no heavy lateral loads occur and there is no accident. Then in another bay, under ostensibly similar conditions, concrete piles up too fast against a bulkhead, or several buggies come to a sudden stop at the same time, and forms unexpectedly collapse. Or perhaps minor differences in assembly details result in localized weaknesses.

So many formwork failures or construction failures associated with formwork have been reported that it is possible here only to summarize the types of failure, and to describe a few accidents of each type. The cases have been grouped, according to their probable causes, in the following categories:

1. Overloading, either vertical or lateral
2. Inadequate bracing for lateral forces
3. Connection and bearing details
4. Unstable bearing support for formwork
5. Premature form removal
6. Reshoring problems
7. New or untried methods.

As with other construction failures there may be incidents with multiple causes, or accidents whose real cause is not divulged. Such cases have been included in the most nearly applicable grouping.

OVERLOADING

Vertical Loads

Simple vertical overloading of forms is not too common a cause of form failures today, perhaps because it is reasonably easy to estimate vertical loads and to provide support for them. An early case was the eight-story Bellefield Apartment Building in Pittsburgh where a section of the roof fell in 1903 as it was being placed.[111, 112] Slabs spanned 12 ft 9 in. and were reinforced with expanded metal. The spliced wood shores were defective and broke when the load was applied. Since the roof was being concreted ahead of some of the lower floors to enclose the building before bad weather, the panel fell two or three stories before striking another slab. The second slab broke under the impact, and the entire mass continued all the way to the basement. Apparently there were other weaknesses besides the shoring.

In an (unpublished) incident at Yonkers, N.Y., in 1957 a large garage was being built when a single bay of forms of the first floor collapsed. Preliminary investigation indicated poor soil bearing for the mudsills, but a casual remark by a worker explained the failure more accurately. A 7½ cu yd truck loaded with concrete had backed up to the form and dumped its entire load in the center of a 15x30-ft panel already filled with its design load of 12 cu yd of concrete.

It is difficult to say how many failure cases attributed to other causes may have involved an actual overloading. Certainly unequal settlement of form supports may cause local overloading of individual shores. The same is true when bent or defective individual shores are used; if they cannot take their full load, the adjoining shores may be overloaded. Eccentricity of load application sharply reduces the buckling load of tubular shores thus resulting in overload.

Lateral Pressure of Concrete

Inadequate provision for the lateral pressure of freshly placed concrete is more likely to cause bulges and deformations which go

Figure 5.1—Formwork collapse at New York Coliseum where double-tier shoring gave way, apparently due to lateral thrust imposed by concrete placing activities.

unreported, although not unnoticed, than to trigger any newsworthy accident. Although the exact variation of lateral pressure is a matter to be resolved by further research, ACI Committee 347 has developed formulas[113] for pressure which may be safely used in designing the forms for vertical concrete members.

The temperature and vertical rate of placement in the forms are factors influencing the lateral pressure development, and if temperature drops during concreting, the rate of placement often has to be slowed down to prevent a buildup of lateral pressure which will overload the forms. Fortunately it is possible to observe the deflection of vertical forms and to slow or stop concreting when deflections become too large; this is another reason why failures from overpressure are seldom reported.

A special problem exists when edge beam and lintel forms are supported without diagonal bracing on vertical T-head shores. Lateral pressure against the exterior vertical form results in lateral drift of the form and expensive later chipping of protruding concrete faces. Shore heads are commonly extended on the outside to accommodate knee braces that will maintain form alignment.

INADEQUATE BRACING FOR LATERAL FORCES

A system of formwork to receive wet concrete high above grade or above the previously constructed floor is not the most stable structure. The weight is almost entirely at the top and is supported by an array of posts which are not rigidly connected to the form at the top or to the floor at the bottom. The lack of diagonal bracing is a common threat in such formwork where lateral loads such as wind, cable tensions, starting and stopping of equipment, and dumping of concrete are likely to occur. The case was admirably put by Edward Godfrey[7] nearly 30 years ago:

> It is not sufficient that bracing be supplied only where definite lateral forces exist, such as the bracing to resist wind stresses: there is a general need of lateral rigidity in any structure where compressive stresses are carried. The points of these members where they receive their loads, and, if they are slender, intermediate points must be held against lateral displacement. By observing these precautions, very light structures may be made to safely carry very heavy loads; by ignoring them, very heavy structures may collapse from their own dead weight.

His remarks apply particularly to formwork, although they were made in relation to all types of construction.

The following cases show that insufficient diagonal bracing is a common cause of contemporary formwork troubles. Note that most of these collapses involve shoring 20 to 30 ft high, some in double-tier arrangement, some apparently in a single tier of extended shores.

RESERVOIR ROOF, SANTA MONICA, CALIFORNIA—1949

Forms supporting a 40x85-ft section of newly placed roof deck over a reservoir in Santa Monica, Calif., failed in 1949.[114] Columns in steel forms some 20 ft high were being placed together with the 5-in. deck. Forms were supported on typical extended jack shores. Failure photographs show that duck boards were used as runways for rubber-tired buggies. Jack shoring of adjacent forms that did not fail was kicked out of plumb, and there was no indication of diagonal bracing. Columns remained erect after the slab area collapsed.

PARKE-BERNET GALLERIES, NEW YORK, N.Y.—1949[115]

A five-story plus penthouse building was under construction when a 39x76-ft section of the fifth floor fell. Columns were spaced 19½x22½ ft on centers, except under the collapsed area—two center bays on the third floor—where columns were omitted for a sales auditorium two stories (22 ft) high with no obstructing columns. The 7-in. slab was supported by ⅝-in. plywood decking resting on 2x4 wood stringers, 12 in. on centers, extending to within 1 in. of girders bordering the open well. These forms were carried on patented 8-ft adjustable shores supported on 4x4's 14 ft long, resting on the third floor. At the 14-ft level there was horizontal 4x4 bracing one way and plank the other. Horizontal bracing in two directions was provided both above and below this 14-ft level, but there is no record of any diagonal bracing.

On the morning of June 15, 1949, the concrete had been placed in three bays of the fifth floor adjacent to the auditorium. After lunch, the auditorium slab was being placed when it suddenly gave way, and the load dropped to the unshored third floor. Failure was localized to the area being placed, and the mass was successfully carried by the completed, unshored third floor below. Photographs indicate that concrete was being placed by large wheel buggies running on duck boards. Failure area was limited almost exactly to the entire form on high shores.

OIL STORAGE TANK, EVERETT, MASSACHUSETTS—1953[116]

Four identical petroleum storage tanks, 180x168 ft and 30 ft high, were being built. The 10-in. flat plate roofs of these tanks were to be supported on 2-ft exterior walls and 63 round columns spaced 21x18 ft on centers. Columns were being cast in cylindrical steel forms, with capitals and drop panels cast with roof slab.

At the time of failure one tank had half of its roof cast and stripped and the other half partly formed. On Oct. 3, 1953, another tank was within a few minutes of having half its roof placed—some 400 cu yd of concrete—when a failure occurred in the wood formwork. The ⅝-in. plywood forms were supported on 3x4 joists 16 in. apart, spanning 5 ft 3 in. These joists were carried by double 2x8 stringers supported on spliced 4x4 posts 6 ft apart, 30 ft high. The posts were braced horizontally with four sets of braces in two directions. There was also some diagonal bracing. Similar supports had been used with success on the adjacent tank. The entire form collapsed, leaving the previously concreted columns standing. A more adequate bracing system at least could have limited the failure area.

An exhaustive investigation failed to uncover the exact cause of the formwork failure at the New York Coliseum described below. However, the district attorney for New York County expressed the opinion[117] that a "horizontal or oblique thrust on the main exhibition floor" produced by vibration, starting and stopping of power buggies, and other construction activity probably triggered the collapse. "If there had been sufficient diagonal, horizontal, and end bracing of the temporary supporting structure," his report concluded, "the collapse could have been prevented entirely or, at the worst, its area held to a minimum."

NEW YORK COLISEUM, NEW YORK, N.Y.—1955[118, 119]

About 10,000 sq ft of formwork for the main exhibition floor of the New York Coliseum gave way. The floor was a waffle flat slab; the immediate area of failure also had several deep girders framing out the main stairway and escalator opening. Form shoring was built in two tiers with maximum height 22 ft. The bottom tier consisted of wood posts spaced on a 2½x4-ft grid with a line of horizontal bracing in two directions and some diagonal bracing. The upper tier, seated on a cap sill, consisted of adjustable pipe shores with flat cap plates to support the timber joists. Similar form design had been used on this project for some 60 placements of similar extent, and some of these had also been 22 ft high. About 700 cu yd of a scheduled 1000 cu yd placement had been placed by 2 P.M. when failure occurred without any warning (Figure 5.1). Two inspectors were on the deck as it failed. Form watchers under the form, however, were almost entirely away at the time. Placing was by power buggies running at a reported 12 mph on timber duck boards, each carrying 12 cu ft of mix.

After the Coliseum accident, increased diagonal bracing was placed in all remaining shoring, and the collapsed area was rebuilt with new two-tier shoring braced horizontally and diagonally in both tiers. Later work was performed with slower speeds on the buggies, rubber cushions under the duck boards where they rested on the completed concrete floor edges, U-shaped top caps on the shores to permit horizontal nailing into the joists, and diagonal ties for the pipe shores.

Insufficiently braced high shoring, this time to a height of 30 ft, was blamed along with vibrating equipment in a much smaller accident that took no death toll.

Parking Garage, Jackson, Mississippi—1956[120]

A 20x30-ft bay of concrete slab that had just been placed on metal pan forms collapsed while it was being vibrated. The forms were supported on 4x6-in. timbers carried by screw-jack pipe shores 30 ft high, *braced horizontally only at midhight.* The d:rector of the Jackson building department said the collapse was probably caused by action of the vibrating and placing equipment; he thought the lack of diagonal bracing was a contributing factor.

The following incident which took four lives was called an "act of God," by the coroner's jury, but the evident lack of diagonal bracing would seem to make this an unfair indictment of the Deity.

Factory Roof, Montreal, P.Q.—1959[121, 122]

Near the end of a 750-cu yd placement on the roof of an addition to the Johnson and Johnson, Ltd. plant, a 120x160-ft section of forms and freshly placed concrete collapsed. The 9½-in. flat slab roof, 20 ft above grade, was being built in 30x32-ft bays. Forms were supported on slender pipe scaffolding 20 ft high *with one level of horizontal bracing.* The shores rested on 6x8 sills set in a compacted run-of-crusher base layer. This placement was the fourth of five sections; the first three had been installed without incident.

Concrete was being placed from two truck cranes; at the time of collapse a 45-mph wind was also blowing. Witnesses testified to checking all supports of the forms, and blamed the wind action against tarpaulins which had been slung to cover the open side of the building.

Construction workers threatened a strike following the accident described below, in which a foreman was crushed to death and 15 others were injured.

Georgia Power Company Office Building, Atlanta, Georgia— 1959[123, 124]

A 21x27-ft bay of the second floor on this 22-story office building collapsed and fell 26 ft to the first floor, carrying the concreting crew with it. As workers rushed in to help the trapped men, a second bay collapsed on them.

The metal pans forming a 4-in. slab with 14-in. ribs were supported on plywood deck, which was carried by metal pipe scaffolding spaced 4 ft on centers both ways. The scaffold legs had been extended above and below the frames with the usual attachments to make the 26-ft height. Some of the top extensions were observed bent out of shape after the collapse. Concrete was being hoisted by bucket and moved across the deck by push-buggy.

Although the cause of the foregoing failure was not disclosed, it has been included here because of the high shoring involved. It may be well to note, also, that slender tubular metal shoring is particularly vulnerable to eccentric loading because of the geometry of its cross

Figure 5.2—Atlanta building after collapse of formwork which had been supported on tubular metal scaffolding. A foreman was crushed to death and 15 workers injured in the accident.

section, and eccentricities may be introduced when tubular supports are bent or otherwise damaged (cf. p. 97). Numerous precautions in the recently recommended safety code for vertical shoring[125] are well worth studying.

Improper and inadequate bracing together with improper installation of formwork were blamed by the Toronto coroner's jury investigating the next described accident.[126]

TORONTO SUBWAY, TORONTO, ONTARIO—1961[126–128]

Facing material for the massive roof slab form (see Figure 5.3) was ⅝-in. plywood in the shape of an arch, fastened to wood stringers and supported by a series of built-up wood frames. The frames were supported on adjustable shores set on an intermediate slab, with a corresponding set of shores beneath the intermediate slab. There was no diagonal bracing between the frames or shores, and the frames were not braced against longitudinal movement.

A bulkhead at one end of the section was braced against longitudinal movement, but as the concrete was placed, the load against the bulkhead caused the bracing to deflect, permitting movement of the bulkhead. Apparently this movement caused some of the jack shores to slip or tip, and the whole form collapsed. Some witnesses claimed that there was actually no reason for the forms to fail—60 or 70 previous placements had been made in a similar way without difficulty.

The coroner's jury, following the longest inquest in Ontario history, said that the collapsed formwork was inadequately and improperly braced, and that the transit commission and two construction firms were to blame. The jury described existing local regulations as "very incomplete" and urged adoption and enforcement of the National Building Code of Canada.

The foregoing incidents are typical of the many illustrating the need for greater stability in the temporary formwork structure. One step in this direction is to cast columns at least a day ahead of the floor. This provides considerable stiffness against lateral sway (although it is no guarantee against failure as the case on p. 99 demonstrates). The unit labor cost of placing the concrete may be increased, but the small expenditure is cheap insurance. Actually, in multistory flat plate designs, many contractors are convinced that if the columns are cast as soon as the deck is installed and before any slab reinforcement is placed, a saving will result in the reduction of labor of casting columns through the concentrated maze of rods at the columns and in the easier control of bleeding which reduces finishing time and costs. At the same time, the columns are permitted to take their shrinkage, a procedure usually specified but often not obeyed.

Stability of formwork can also be improved in the form planning stage, by making adequate provision for bracing to withstand foreseeable lateral loads. ACI Committee 347 has recommended some minimum values of lateral loading[113] to be used in the absence of specific information or governing specifications as to this loading.

CONNECTION AND BEARING DETAILS

Forms are supported on continuous framework, and, like all continuously supported structures, must have uniformly fixed reactions. As the plastic concrete covers the forms, reactions on the posts change, and there is a strong possibility of upward movement at posts beyond the area covered by the concrete. Careful nailing for uplift resistance must be provided. Wedging posts to level up forms is an operation which must be done under careful supervision, to avoid leaving posts disconnected from the deck. This would provide a possible beginning of failure if the reaction thereon became negative.

In many cases these inadequacies in formwork details lead to bulges and misalignment rather than to collapse. For example, there was a case where the stairwell openings in a steel frame building were not of sufficient dimension. In this job, forms had been suspended by tie wire from the steel beams. To reduce time and labor in stripping, the wood joists were hung by wires bent over the top beam flanges all on one side of the beam. The weight of the wet concrete caused a torsional pull at one edge of the steel beams. Concrete hardened around the twisted steel beams. Exposure of the steel showed that top flanges at midspan were from ½ to ¾ in. out of level and the faces of the concrete fireproofing had drifted into the clear width required for stairways.

The frequent necessity for chipping out concrete in all shaftways had been taken as a normal expectation. This error in unbalanced loadings on steel beams was then explained at a large office building in New York, and the contractor measured the edge elevations of the

Figure 5.3—Transverse and longitudinal sections (opposite page) of form and shoring arrangement for Toronto subway in the area of collapse. Drawings from Engineering News-Record, August 10, 1961 (McGraw-Hill, Inc.).

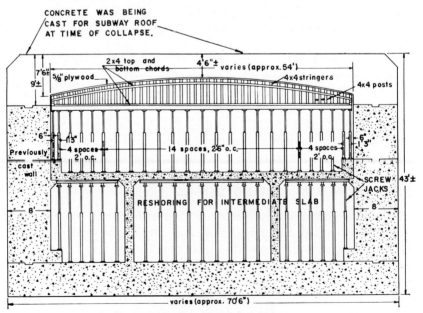

TRANSVERSE   CROSS   SECTION

steel beams during concreting and found that all the beams were twisting. When these results were publicized, orders were issued by the New York building department that tie supports must be alternated and the difficulty has been eliminated. Of course there is an extra cost of stripping, since half of the wires must be cut before the joist can be rolled out and stripped. However, the cost of chipping and other construction adjustment is eliminated—a net saving in over-all cost.

In an unpublished incident in Miami, Fla., in 1957, open-web steel joists used for form support rotated as concrete was placed on the form. This action was similar to the unbalanced loading on the steel beams described above, when form hangers were all placed on one side of the beam.

In a seven-story wall-bearing apartment house in Arlington, Va. (1960), a 24x30-ft section of the first floor gave way during the concreting. The slab was reinforced with paper-backed mesh which also acted as the form and was tied to open-web steel joists. Rotation of the joist supports had occurred since no ties were installed to connect joists together and provide resistance to overturning of the end joist under unbalanced load.

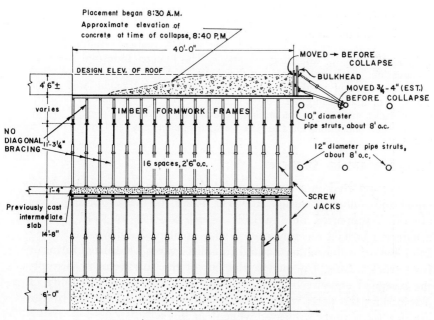

LONGITUDINAL CROSS SECTION

In Washington, D.C., in 1959, flat plate forms were supported on expanded steel joist stringers. These stringers were cambered for bending deflection but did not take care of the shear compression at the column support area where the column form was more rigid than the shoring support, so that a lip in the concrete ceiling surfaces resulted. This required expensive grinding and plastering to provide the desired smooth ceiling.

Collapse of part of a dome roof for a water tank at Melrose, Ill., Nov. 21, 1957, was reported[129] under the headline "puzzling failure." The tank, 150 ft in diameter, and 30 ft high, had had an 8-ft band of its dome roof concreted along the ring girder, and concrete was being placed for the adjoining band when a 16x100-ft section fell, killing one and injuring eight. Investigators blamed the falsework but were unable to determine an exact cause. Similar form design had been successfully used in many previous projects. The case is mentioned here, because of some similarities to a more recent incident in which details of the formwork assembly were blamed for collapse.

DOME TANK ROOF, HILLSBORO, OREGON—1962[130, 131]

It was mid-December when workers finishing the domed roof of a 100-ft diameter water tank fell 65 ft to the ground (five died) as formwork collapsed under the center. An outer ring of the dome, concreted the day before the accident, remained in place, showing no signs of movement. The dome, 10 in. thick at the outside and 4 in. at the center, was to be prestressed before becoming self supporting.

Forms were shored with several tiers of 4x4 timbers, equipped with jacks at the top for adjusting elevations. The Oregon Industrial Accident Commission which investigated did not report a specific cause, but cited two main areas of weakness; most likely cause, they thought, was in the difficulty of maintaining a rigid connection at the top of falsework columns where jacks are set to make fine adjustments in column height. Weak end-to-end connections of the 4x4 vertical shores may also have been a factor.

STABLE BEARING SUPPORT

Posts supported on a lower completed floor can be assumed to have equal and uniform bearing. However, forms for the lowest slab level are often supported on "mudsills" which are not on solid ground, usually on backfill recently placed with great probability of softening from flow of water, either natural run-off or wash water from forms or from truck mixers. Unequal settlement of the sills seriously disrupts the designed equality of post reactions and with good possibility of overloading the posts which do not settle as the load carried by the exterior line of posts is released when their sills settle.

A common cause of structural defects is the practice of placing mudsills on frozen ground. As construction progresses frost protection heaters and dripping from concrete placement soften the ground, causing unwanted sags in the supported structure. Typical example was a three-tier school built in Brooklyn, N.Y., in 1956. The long span slabs were found dished in decreasing amounts from first floor to roof, but in sympathetic shapes. Investigation showed that the lowest level was supported on mudsills which settled, and the upper layers were shored on precut posts set on the deflected slabs. No check of floor level had been made; the slabs were merely made a uniform thickness of concrete on the respective forms.

Even when working on apparently solid ground, bearing support problems may arise, as in the case of a highway overpass near Cleveland, Ohio, which collapsed during construction in 1961.[132] One hundred tons of freshly placed concrete, nine workers, and a heavy concrete finisher fell 18 ft. Falsework supporting the bridge was on beams standing on the existing pavement beneath. The pavement sagged and the falsework gave way resulting in $50,000 damage.

Pile supports for falsework may likewise prove vulnerable, as the following case demonstrates.

ARCH BRIDGE, SPOKANE, WASHINGTON—1917[133, 134]

On February 6, 1917, the Post St. Bridge across the Spokane River collapsed without warning while one rib was being concreted. Twin-rib arches of 250-ft span were being erected on framed timber falsework which was supported on timber pile bents supposedly driven to rock in the river bottom. There were 18 bents, spaced about 12 ft center to center; each bent contained six carrying piles and one tie pile, was capped with 12x12's.

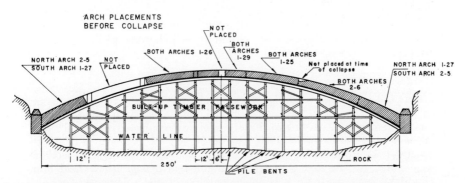

Figure 5.4—Falsework arrangement for Post St. Bridge in Spokane, which collapsed during concreting in 1917. Placement sequence is indicated on the drawing.

Concrete was being placed in transverse units with sectional openings between as shown in Figure 5.4. At the time of collapse, all but one west section and the small crown key section slated for final placement had been concreted.

High water conditions prevailed on the river, and the engineer who designed both bridge and falsework had drowned the previous week. Half-yard batches of concrete were being dropped into the remaining west section from heights ranging between 9 and 15 ft just before the collapse. The foreman had examined the falsework about 30 minutes earlier and found everything "normal and undisturbed."

Subsequent investigations brought out that the piles, although allegedly driven to refusal, had little or no penetration, and spiked bracing was the only means of preventing the frame from kicking off the rock surface. The piles were "shamefully small," and the upper falsework frame of inadequate size. Rib sections as placed were too long, and the nonsymmetrical placing sequence probably distorted falsework; these factors along with general flimsiness of frame and impact from dumping probably caused the wreck.

PREMATURE FORM REMOVAL

Premature stripping of forms has caused numerous failures, not only in terms of collapses but in the often unreported sagging of partially cured concrete, and in the development of hairline cracks that cause serious maintenance problems in the later life of the structure. During the earlier history of concrete construction, when cold weather work was frequently inadequately protected, there were many failures when the forms were pulled. There was a widespread failure to recognize that satisfactory temperature as well as time requirements must be met before removing forms. Whether to attribute these incidents to "early form removal" or to "cold weather" presents the problem in drawing a fine line of distinction . . . and some of the cases described under cold weather concreting problems might equally well be described here.

No cold weather problems were involved in the following "unavoidable accident," as the coroner called it, which took place Sept. 11, 1911.

FOUR-STORY BUILDING, WINNIPEG, MANITOBA—1911[135]

This slab and girder building was designed for 200–250 psf live loads on its four floors, and the roof was designed for 40 psf. Supporting columns for the roof were cast August 15, the roof was concreted August 18 and 19, and a built-up roof installed August 21 and 22. Nine bays, 23x19 ft, collapsed when the shores were being removed September 7. Two workers were killed by the falling material but the fourth floor below held firm. Hindsight suggests there was some warning of the roof weakness . . . workers said later that the wedges seemed to tighten up after each hammer blow. Finally when extra heavy blows were applied, the shores were released and the roof came down too.

Whether this concrete roof would ever have been strong enough for formwork removal is open to question; columns apparently crushed in the failure too.

Other accounts of form removal involve clear cases of carelessness, ignorance, or misunderstanding. In the Paddington Apartment Building in Chicago, 1902, forms were hung from the 10-in. I-beams but were also supported by diagonal timber frames wedged to the completed floors.[136] The fourth floor concrete was 21 days old and was being loaded with a 6-in. layer of cinder concrete filling when inexperienced workmen removed some of the timber supports which were intended to remain two or three weeks longer. The ensuing collapse left a hole 40 ft long in the top slab and a smaller one all the way to the basement 40 ft below, as lower slabs gave way under extra impact load.

A partial collapse of the Bridgman Building occurred in Philadelphia in 1907.[137] Shores were removed after 5½ days instead of the 2 weeks required by city specifications. Reportedly the command to knock out "every other one" of the shores was relayed to some workmen whose command of English was limited; they simply knocked out all the shores.

Two men were killed by the roof collapse which followed form removal in a two story garage at Ogden, Utah, in 1914.[138] The concrete had been in place 10 days. It had been raining, and the form removal was a "make work" operation to keep the men busy.

These cases are but a few of the many accidents involving problems with too-early form removal. Early form removal is usually desirable from the contractor's point of view because he can reuse the forms. Time of removal, however, should be specified in the contract documents by the architect-engineer, or made subject to his approval, because of the danger of injury to concrete which may not have attained full strength, or which may be overloaded in stripping or subsequent construction operations, as well as the danger to human life as in the collapses just described. ACI Committee 347[113] has suggested minimum requirements for time of form removal on jobs where the engineer has made no provision for approval of shore and form removal based on strength and other conditions peculiar to the job. The periods recommended are qualified to be the "cumulative number of days or fractions thereof, not necessarily consecutive, during which the temperature of the concrete is above 50 F."

RESHORING

Premature reshoring and inadequate size and spacing of reshores have been responsible for a number of construction failures. The problem is particularly troublesome in multistory flat slab structures which are designed for a relatively light live load. The accumulated load of slabs freshly placed and partially cured together with construction live load may be larger than the load which a floor is designed to carry when it has developed its full strength. Usually only part of that strength is developed when construction of the next story begins. The following is a case in point.

Underground Municipal Parking Garage, Newark, New Jersey— 1960[139, 140]

About 120 cu yd of concrete in the roof of a three-story garage fell as the men were screeding the completed surface of an 18-in. slab designed to carry 4 ft of earth. The fall on the second floor slab, then 2 weeks old, also broke out the same area, 2000 sq ft, and cracked the slab below. Concrete was made with high early strength cement, and both floors had been reshored with steel pipe screw jacks.

Investigation by a city building official placed responsibility for origin of the collapse on careless reshoring practices. Temporary loads on the reshored slabs were far greater than their permanent design loads. Some of the tubular screw-jack reshores appeared to have been bent before installation; some were not carefully plumbed. These two defects both produce eccentric loading, which leads to buckling at a fraction of the rated load capacity of tubular shores.

A year later the concrete supplier and two employees as well as three men associated with a testing laboratory were indicted for conspiracy to cheat and defraud the public; the indictment charged them with conspiring to furnish concrete of incorrect mix proportions without the high early strength cement as specified.

Since reshoring is such a highly critical operation, it should be planned in advance and approved by the designer of the structure. In the study of form removal and reshoring, live loads for which the structure is designed, as well as the actual strength of the partially cured concrete must be considered. Allowance must be made for any additional live or dead loads to be imposed as construction continues, and then a reshoring system capable of taking any loads to be imposed can be designed.

NEW OR UNTRIED METHODS OF FORMING

Many of the previously described formwork troubles involved designs, systems, or details that had been successfully used many times before the one case that brought accident or failure. In contrast are the accidents which occur with relatively new forming materials or methods, or work on new types of structures, before there has been opportunity to fully prove these techniques. No doubt these are frequently cases of overloading, arising from a failure to understand structural action of the forms.

There has as yet been no official explanation of the following failure of an unusual steel forming system.

ROCKET TEST CELL, TULLAHOMA, TENNESSEE—1962[141, 142]

Nearly 900 tons of concrete fell when concreting was in progress on the first of six wedge shaped sections of the roof of a rocket test silo. The 9 ft thick roof slab was to cover an underground silo, more than 100 ft in diameter and 250 ft deep.

Triangular steel shoring trusses cantilevered 34½ ft from the silo wall were spaced radially at 11¼ deg around the circular opening. Trusses were 30 ft

Figure 5.5—Remaining formwork at rocket test cell, showing extent of collapse. Main supporting members were triangular shoring trusses, cantilevered from the silo wall. Light timbers atop the steel trusses carried plywood decking.

deep at the wall where they were bolted to plates anchored in the concrete. None of these anchor plates pulled out of the concrete at the time of failure. The bottom chords of the trusses needed some lateral bracing since they were in compression, and this may have caused enough distortion to start failure. The interior edge of the slab, which is a central opening 39 ft in diameter, was formed with circular wood forms, braced with wales and strongbacks. Light timbers were placed on top of the steel truss supports to hold plywood decking.

Another unusual (in its time) forming technique for a dome roof over a linen supply service sorting and marking room met with several difficulties in an attempt to conserve materials under wartime restrictions.

INFLATED FORMS FOR DOME, LOS ANGELES, CALIFORNIA—1943[143, 144]

Inflated canvas bags were used as forms for a 100 ft diameter dome roof whose maximum ceiling height was 32 ft. Concrete was to be pneumatically applied in layers ¼ in. thick, 5 or 6 ft wide, completely surrounding the form. Each ring was being built up to about 1¼ in. thickness before starting a new ring. After this first layer was completed, it was planned to deflate the form, place a layer of reinforcement, and then shotcrete an outer layer of roof concrete covering the steel.

An initial local failure was attributed to overloading the forms; work was resumed after repairs of the balloon form. A second collapse came after the first mortar coat had been completed; one of three blowers that kept the bag inflated failed, and the pressure was lowered too much before another blower could be put into service. The green concrete cracked and the entire structure fell.

Shotcreting in the opposite direction—inside an inflated form—was being attempted in the following more recent incident, but with similar unfortunate results.

INFLATED DOME FORM, CINCINNATI, OHIO—1962[145]

Concrete was being sprayed onto the inside of a nylon-reinforced vinyl form held up by air pressure. The form shaped a dome roof, 23 ft high, covering a 100 ft square warehouse for the Morton Salt Company. Three applications of sprayed concrete were planned to build the shell to 2½ in. thick. The vinyl form was to remain in place as a waterproof covering for the dome.

A single spray gun had been applying the concrete; the shell was about 1½ in. thick, with a total of 55 cu yd of concrete in place when complete collapse occurred. Apparently the slick surfaced plastic failed to bond with the concrete. As small pieces of concrete fell, one ripped a hole in the plastic, and this triggered the collapse as supporting air pressure was lost.

Plans for rebuilding included an increase of dome height to provide a steeper roof slope, modifications in the reinforcement pattern, and use of a cotton backed fabric for the form, to improve bond with the concrete. (The contractor had apparently used this method successfully before with a cotton backed form.) The local building department also decided to require a deflection detector and a warning device to signal any decrease in air pressure.

TOWARD IMPROVED FORMWORK PRACTICES

A long series of serious and costly formwork failures, of which the cases cited are but a sampling, brought increasing awareness of the need for better, safer forming practices. Piecemeal regulations were being enacted locally in response to the tragic occurrences, but there seemed to be no comprehensive over-all standard or guide for formwork design and erection. Recognizing the need of contractors, engineers, architects, and inspectors for some readily available guide to good practice, the American Concrete Institute in 1955 organized Committee 347,* Formwork for Concrete, on which the author has served since its inception. The committee first studied lateral pressure on formwork, then surveyed existing formwork practices, before taking up its major task of developing specifications for design and construction of formwork. The efforts of Committee 347 culminated in the preparation of a recommended practice that in 1963 became an ACI standard.

The committee also directed preparation of *Formwork for Concrete*,[146] which is a how-to-do-it manual expanding the concise statements of the standard into detailed data and suggestions directly usable by form designers and builders as well as supervising architects and engineers. Both of these publications emphasize improved quality of formwork as well as its stability and safety. Thus considerable progress has been made toward better forming practices; yet much remains to be done if this accumulated knowledge is to be put into practice.

Some Conclusions to Be Drawn

Sound principles of formwork design and construction—properly applied—will remedy many of the problems that have been discussed. To cover these fully would be to duplicate the work already done by ACI Committee 347. However, several significant points which come to mind as a result of the author's many analyses of formwork failures are briefly stated.

1. Formwork design weakness is commonly in details rather than the main structural members, since designs similar to those

---

* Formerly designated Committee 622.

involved in failures have been used successfully on other occasions.

2. Details which are difficult to perform, such as the overhead driving of nails to connect flat cap plates of a shore to an un-loaded wood joist, will not be properly performed and may start a failure. Such items should be eliminated in the planning stage.

3. High shoring becomes particularly susceptible to failure when not adequately braced diagonally.

4. Shock and vibration from the use of duck board runways must be controlled.

5. Power buggies, in synchronism at high speeds, impose a lateral force which must be provided for in the design and details.

6. Forms are continuously supported structures and must be provided with uniform bearing at each support; otherwise settled mudsills or shrinkage at timber post splices will completely upset the computed reactions, with possible overloading of some posts.

7. Wedging of posts to counteract compression under load must be done under proper supervision so that a previously properly assembled form support is not disrupted.

A repetition of the editorial warning in 1903[5] covers the most important item: "some degree of skilled labor should be employed, or . . . at least the entire work should be under strict and constant supervision by skilled foremen, architects, or engineers."

6

Durability of Concrete and Its Compatibility with Other Materials

DETERIORATION MAY RESULT from influences either within the concrete itself or inherent in the environment to which it is exposed. The gradual or progressive deterioration or weakening of concrete in service—unlike many of the types of failure treated in this monograph—is a subject that is receiving continuing attention and has been subjected to extensive professional and industrial research. The 500-page book by Mall previously cited,[14] for example, deals primarily with this topic. ACI Committee 201[147] recently presented a summary of much of the current knowledge on durability of concrete in service. The committee listed durability problems under the following headings, explaining the basic mechanism of deterioration in each case, and also suggesting the proportioning, placing, curing, and maintenance practices best suited to overcoming the difficulty.

> *Freezing and Thawing*—Wet concrete exposed to repeated cycles of freezing and thawing is sometimes damaged or destroyed. It is believed the principal force responsible for frost damage in ordinary concretes under usual winter exposures is internal hydraulic pressure caused by an expanding ice-water system during freezing.

> *Ice Removal Agents*—Use of sodium or calcium chloride and other chemicals for ice removal has caused surface

115

disintegration of many pavements; pitting and scaling are the chief manifestations. The mechanism of damage is not fully understood, but it is believed to be physical rather than chemical, since deicing materials of widely varying chemical and physical properties are capable of causing the damage.

Aggressive Chemical Agents—There are some chemical environments under which the useful life of even the best concrete will be shortened. Concrete is rarely attacked by dry, solid chemicals, but many corrosive chemicals in solution above some minimum concentration produce significant attack on concrete. Brine solutions or sea water which attack the reinforcing steel as well as the concrete present special complications.

Abrasion of Concrete—Abrasion may result from foot or vehicular traffic on floors or pavements, or from wind- or water-borne particles* striking either vertical or horizontal surfaces. Damage or failure may be either structural or functional (as an example of the latter, dusting of floors in an area where airborne particles contaminate materials or operations in process).

Corrosion of Reinforcement—Where concrete cover is of insufficient depth or unsatisfactory quality, reinforcing steel may be corroded by chemical, electrical, or water influence. Corrosion weakens the steel, causes expansion which may split or further damage the covering concrete.

Reactive Aggregates—With certain combinations of cement and aggregate, internal chemical changes within the concrete result in cracks and fractures, often accompanied by surface crazing and spalling, and consequent loss of strength. The most common reaction is one between alkali of the cement and certain siliceous constituents of the aggregate, allowing the formation of an expansive gel.

It is neither necessary nor desirable to duplicate the work of Committee 201, but a few cases of failure will be presented to illustrate some of these points. Many failed surfaces or structures, as the cases

---

* Erosion in hydraulic structures is discussed in the report by ACI Committee 210, "Erosion Resistance of Concrete in Hydraulic Structures," ACI JOURNAL, *Proceedings* V. 52, No. 3, Nov. 1955, pp. 259-271.

indicate, have been subjected to more than one of these influences. For example, ice removal agents are commonly applied in areas where alternation of freezing and thawing can be expected, or maritime structures may be subjected near the water line to alternate freezing and thawing, chemically aggressive sea water, plus erosion or abrasion from tide action.

OCEAN WATER

Used in Mixing Concrete

Despite several technical publications that "prove" satisfactory concrete made with sea water, actual inspections of structures where salt intentionally or otherwise got into the concrete mix show that only trouble and ultimate failure result from such use. Of course where fresh water is not available and the structures are for temporary occupancy, use of salt water in the mix is expedient and may even be economically sound, but it will not produce sound concrete. The condition of carefully designed and carefully supervised construction of concrete bridges and homes in Bermuda, in the southern Florida areas, and in other places, where sea water is used for washing the aggregates and often also replaces the fresh water specified for mixing, indicates especially the vulnerability of embedded reinforcement and metal conduits.

A single example of some two-story concrete housing at Key West, Fla., illustrates the difficulties that may be expected from sea water concrete. Units were built in 1950 under rigid federal specifications; the aggregate was taken from the ocean and washed with sea water after crushing. Indirect proof that brackish water or sea water was used for mixing came from the small amount of fresh water metered from the navy pipe line, the only source of fresh water. After about 3 years, the electric wiring shorted and considerable spalling of the ceilings made occupancy hazardous. Exposure showed that corrosion of the conduits had pinched off the wire insulation. The rusting of the reinforcing rods and conduit had pushed the covering concrete out of ceilings and floors.

Considerable reconstruction was necessary, but as long as the high humidity of the area permits moisture penetration into the concrete similar troubles will continue. During the complete inspection of several apartment buildings, it was observed that a number of the rooms, at random locations, had been air-conditioned by the occupants. This control of humidity had reduced the amount of moisture absorbed by the concrete in these rooms, and there were practically no spalls or corrosion troubles in these rooms.

Action on Concrete Structures

The danger from ion exchange in concrete immersed in sea water was described in a report by Professor Brazier[148] of the University of Aberdeen in the 1880's, when he investigated the reason for the pervious nature of the concrete graving dock in the Aberdeen harbor. He warned that over-calcined cement used in concrete exposed to sea water will absorb magnesia and cause surface disintegration of the concrete which in turn exposes more surface to the same action. Similar trouble was reported at many harbor works in England, and Vicat also came to the same conclusion in the study of the complete disintegration of concrete blocks made of lime and artificial pozzolan at Marseilles, Rochefort, Algiers, and Cherbourg, after a few years of exposure to the sea.[149] Reports by Tyler[150] and Halstead and Woodworth[151] are among more recent studies of the effects of ocean water.

Normal chemical action of sea water on concrete from salt spray, plus the action of ice abrasion, tide, and weather is found on many water-front structures. A pier in Santa Monica, Calif., which had to be scrapped in 1920, was inspected by a board of consulting engineers who also investigated the conditions surrounding its construction.[152] They reported the failure was due to gradual decomposing action of the sea water on concrete which was not up to the standard then known to be required of concrete for ocean exposure.

After about 5 years of use, the concrete piles and caps of the trestle bents of the James River Bridge at Newport News, Va., required almost a $1.5 million repair and replacement job in 1955. Some 70 percent of the 2500 piles were found in need of repair and so all the piles were jacketed over the tidal range and the steel sleeves were left as covering.

Similar deterioration was found in the precast concrete piles driven in 1932 near Ocean City, N.J., where, after 25 years, their 22-in. section had become reduced to 12 in. Some 750 piles were repaired by jacketing with pumped grout within a steel sleeve. Continued investigation of the natural aging influences of salt water aided by the physical action of tide and wind has resulted in the recognition that especially dense concretes are necessary and that moisture-tight surfacing is economically advisable.

British investigators studied concrete piles over a 10-year period of controlled sea water exposure followed by 13 years of uncontrolled exposure. They found the major cause of deterioration to be corrosion of the reinforcement, with cement content of the mix and thickness of cover being major factors in determining durability of piles. A high-alumina cement gave the best over-all performance of the several types tested, but it was unsuitable for use in tropical waters.[153]

CHEMICAL AGENTS*

Good quality concrete resists many naturally occurring chemicals; when properly placed, proportioned and cured, it is relatively impervious to most natural waters, soils, and atmospheres. No portland cement concrete, however, will long withstand water of high acid concentration, and in such circumstances appropriate surface covering or treatment must be used. Concrete which is subjected to aggressive solutions under pressure is more vulnerable because the pressures tend to force the aggressive solution into the concrete. When free evaporation can also take place from an exposed face, dissolved salts may accumulate at that face, thus increasing their concentration and possibly resulting in mechanical damage from spalling in addition to chemical attack.

Concrete exposed to farm silage, animal wastes, or organic acids from manufacturing or processing industries is sometimes damaged, though not generally enough to affect structural strength of floors. Hydrogen sulfide in sewage may oxidize to sulfuric acid and cause damage to concrete sewers.[154, 155] Even so small an amount of chemical as the tannin leached from new pine boards used for formwork has affected the hardening of surface concrete and later caused a structurally defective surface subject to deterioration on a dam face.[156] In 1960, a report on abnormally slow set of a concrete tunnel indicated the fault to lie in the use of a lignin base admixture with a cement having a low SO_3 content. To avoid such trouble the Type II cement must have more than 2 percent SO_3.

The Case of the Leaning Chimney

The following strange incident shows how unexpected the chemical attack on concrete and mortar may be, although this experience with a brick chimney is similar to some instances of leaning concrete stacks in Europe.

In 1961, the top 20 ft of a 140-ft radial brick chimney at the power plant of a public hospital in Westchester County, N.Y., started to bend

* Reference 147 lists more than 100 chemical agents, stating their effect if any on concrete.

eastward.[157] An identical chimney next to it, used for the incinerator and coal-fired hot water boiler, remained vertical. The leaning chimney was originally connected to three coal-fired steam boilers which had recently been converted to firing with oil containing considerable sulfur.

The chimney was leaning toward the northeast, the direction of the prevailing windy rain. There was a shoulder in the chimney lining 20 ft from the top, where the wall thickness changed. Driving rain combined with the sulfur fumes, and acid was being collected along the shoulder of the southwest quadrant of the chimney. The sulfuric acid combined with cement in the mortar to form calcium sulfate which takes on water easily and expands as it crystallizes. This expansion enlarged the mortar joints on the southwest quadrant, pushing the chimney over into the wind without forming a single visible crack.

Aggressive Soil and Ground Water

Naturally-occurring aggressive chemicals such as the sulfates of sodium, potassium, and magnesium are sometimes found in soils or waters in which concrete may be placed. The effect of sea water, mildly aggressive because of the soluble sulfate it contains, has already been mentioned, and a few other examples will be cited.

An investigation of concrete deterioration of a foundation for a silo in the Copenhagen harbor in 1957 indicated sulfate attack by the ground water with aggressive carbon dioxide also a primary agent of disintegration. Excessive formation of secondary chemical deposits was found in the concrete exposed to ground water.

Excessive use of calcium chloride for snow removal, together with the leaching of tannic acid from the soil adjacent to new concrete curbs built in 1947 in Syracuse, N.Y., caused complete disintegration of the curbs during their first winter of service. In some lengths, there was no sign of curb above the asphalt pavement after the snows melted in the spring. The remaining concrete was saturated with a tannic acid compound which had been affected by the calcium chloride. Tannic acid wastes in the Providence, R.I., harbor penetrated the adjacent soils to such concentration that the concrete footings for a housing development were affected sufficiently to require removal and replacement. The footings had been built below ground-water level during pumping of the footing pits, but flooded after the concrete looked hard. Most of the concrete remained soft and friable for over 2 weeks after placing. Reconstruction was successful when the pits were kept free of water for about a month after placing.

Food Processing Industries

The action of lactic acid on cement is so rapid and complete that the use of concrete floors in process plants where lactic acid can form is most inadvisable. These include milk pasteurizing plants, cheese manufacturing, breweries, and slaughter houses. Even the joints between the packing house brick used for floor surfacing, unless made of special cements or sulfur compounds, will deteriorate within a year. Where complete sanitary control is required, even a surface defect in the joints permits the accumulation of milk or other wastes which soon alter to lactic acid and further chemical reaction with the cement.

Investigation of complaints of floor leaks in the Bush Terminal structures in Brooklyn showed that circular wood vats with the sides projecting below the vat floor, used for the cooking of candied fruit peels, had permitted the sugar syrup to eat into the concrete floor and form in some cases a complete ring of disintegrated soft concrete through the entire floor thickness.

Sugar or molasses mixed into wet concrete will also inhibit the setting of the cement.[158] Relatively small amounts of sugar may cause considerable damage. For example, one engineer reported several batches of concrete totally useless simply because the lightweight aggregate was shipped in empty sugar sacks.

Cinder concrete, used to a much larger extent in previous years in the New York and Boston areas, is especially vulnerable to chemical action. With even small traces of sulfur present, electrolysis deterioration is rapid on all metallic embedded items. In a floor covering several ammonia compressors and carrying a large bottle washing machine in a New York milk plant, the combination of some milk slop and some ammonia absorption completely disintegrated all of the welded wire mesh reinforcement and all exposures of steel reinforcement and conduit showed so much deterioration that the owner accepted the author's recommendation to abandon the building. Repair costs during occupancy would have far exceeded the replacement cost of a new plant.

REINFORCEMENT CORROSION

Corrosion is usually described as the destruction of a metal by chemical or electrochemical reaction with its environment. Portland cement concrete ordinarily provides good protection of embedded reinforcing steel against corrosion because of the high alkalinity and relatively high electrical resistivity of the concrete in atmospheric exposure. The success of concrete in protecting steel against corrosion depends on quality of the concrete mix, the depth of steel cover, and over-all good workmanship in the concrete construction. Cracking, splitting, honeycomb, poor concrete patches, or generally porous concrete may give access to the moisture, air, and contaminants that cause corrosion.

Bursting of precast concrete beams in the lumber drying kilns at Muskegon, Mich., in 1956 was caused by the expansive forces from the rusting of the reinforcement after the concrete had absorbed moisture from the warm, damp kiln interior.[159] Although the beams were factory cast of dense concrete, the usual cover on the steel in the 14-in. beam web was less than 1 in.—not sufficient to stop air and moisture attacking the steel* and not thick enough to resist the expansive force of the rusting. Actually enough concrete spalled off to permit shear failures in some of the beams, especially with slippage

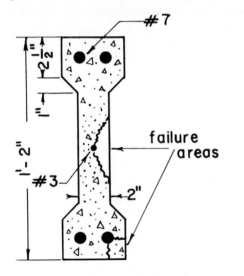

Figure 6.1—Insufficient cover of reinforcement caused steel corrosion and bursting of precast I-beam; the #3 bar in the center of 2-in. web had less than 1 in. of cover. Some of the ⅞-in. steel of the flanges was reduced to ½ in. by corrosion.

of the stressed, corroded reinforcement. Concrete exposed to the high humidities of special uses should be waterproofed with either bituminous or plastic skins and, as a second precaution, concrete cover on the reinforcement should be at least 2 in.

Passage of direct electrical current through concrete or concrete reinforcement may cause rapid and serious corrosion. Such current flow may be caused by electrical leakage or by failure to provide positive and permanent means of grounding electrical systems. Corrosion from this source is a possibility in the presence of any direct current equipment, particularly where there is an electrolyte such as sodium or calcium chloride solutions within or in contact with the concrete.

---

* Less than 1 in. cover is sometimes sufficient where especially rich mixes are used as, for example, the cement mortar for pipe linings.

As early as 1907, the *Engineering News* issued a warning of the danger of corrosion caused by stray currents in wet concrete.[160] Trolley lines were often the current source.

In 1911, severe damage to a packing house near New York City was attributed to electrolytic corrosion, caused by stray current and made more severe because of acids from the rendering process in the moist air of the building.[161] The plant had been completed in October 1906, and in the summer of 1907 cracks appeared on the soffits of various beams and girders, parallel with the reinforcing steel. Cracks had grown steadily worse, to the time of the investigation in 1911; they became wider, and up to 2 in. deep, affecting 3000 lineal ft of beams. Seven columns also developed deep vertical cracks in line with the reinforcing steel. Tough iron oxide, ⅛ to ¼ in. deep, visible on some of the exposed steel, had forced the concrete apart. Most serious injury was beneath rooms cooled by refrigeration, an area where condensation keeps floor and supports damp. There were, however, no cracks in the floor slabs, which were not electrically connected to the girder steel. Nearby trolley lines were at first blamed as source of current, but careful investigators discovered and demonstrated that grounded lighting circuits of the building itself were the cause of the trouble.

A different source of corrosion is the flow of electric current generated within the concrete itself. Electrical potential differences can occur at various points in reinforced concrete because of differences in moisture content, oxygen concentration, electrolyte concentration, and by contact of dissimilar metals. In such concrete a corrosion cell is set up along a steel rod which forms an anode where corrosion occurs. Any moist concrete contains enough electrolyte to conduct a corrosion current, but exposure of concrete to water containing soluble salts is a source of greater danger.

After 2 years use for hide-curing purposes, a reinforced concrete warehouse built in Los Angeles in 1925 developed leaks in the first floor slab making it necessary to waterproof the floor. Five years later pieces of concrete began to fall off the columns and basement walls revealing a most serious condition of corrosion of the reinforcing steel, which threatened the integrity of the building. A complete investigation showed that the curing brine seeping through the concrete had reacted, probably with impurities in the steel, to form minute galvanic cells. Hydrochloric acid formed by electrolytic action had in some cases nearly destroyed the steel without leaving any marks of such destruction on the surface of the concrete.[162]

Exclusion of air by the use ot impermeable, high quality concrete is an effective means of retarding this kind of corrosion.

Corrosion of Prestressing Steel

Hundreds of linear prestressed concrete structures and members, hundreds of circular prestressed tanks, and hundreds of miles of pre-stressed concrete pipe have been built in recent years all over the world. From the fact that the number of reported structural failures in this vast amount of work is so small,[163] it appears that corrosion of prestressing steel is not a common problem. However the possibility of stress corrosion in addition to the types of corrosion already men-tioned for conventional steel reinforcement makes it significant. More-over, because prestressing wire is of such small cross section com-paratively small areas of corrosion can cause serious weakness or rupture. Important lessons have been learned from some failures that have occurred.

PIPE LINE, REGINA, SASKATCHEWAN—1952[163]

Manufacture of 36 in. diameter prestressed concrete pipe to build a 35-mile water supply line for the city of Regina was begun in March, 1952. In mid-November, 1952, a serious leak developed in a 16-ft section during the pressure test of installed pipe. About 5 miles of pipe had already been installed and pipe for about 8 miles more was completed and in storage at the casting plant. Examination of the defective section of pipe, then about 4½ months old, revealed failure of the circumferential prestressed wires due to corrosion; there were hundreds of breaks in this one 16-ft section of pipe. Further examination showed corrosion of the prestressing wires in most of the other sections of pipe, both stored and installed. Pipe production was halted Dec. 23, 1952.

These pipes had been built in three steps:

1. The 2 to 2½ in. thick core containing 24 stressed longitudinal wires was made first with shotcrete mortar containing Type I cement. The core was cured with water spray, 140 F, at least 10 hr.

2. Wire under stress was wound on the hardened core. This was accomplished by drawing a 0.162-in. wire through a 0.142-in. die with power being furnished by the rotating pipe.

3. A ¾-in. cover coat of shotcrete mortar made with sulfate resisting cement was applied. The pipe was water-cured another 10 hr at 140 F.

Following the discovery of corrosion failure, a number of experts were called in to assist in the investigations. Their study brought out the fact that the mortar for the first 84 pipes manufactured consisted of 1 part cement, to about 2.5 parts of sand and 0.42 part water. Mortar for the

Figure 6.2—Laboratory studies undertaken by the Portland Cement Association following the Regina failure revealed longitudinal cracks in all wires which were drawn unlubricated through an uncooled die and then placed in concrete containing calcium chloride. This enlarged photograph shows a typical wire from the Regina project, drawn in the laboratory from 0.162 to 0.142 in., then embedded 6 months in mortar containing 4 percent calcium chloride. The longitudinal crack apparently started at a spot of corrosion adjacent to a void in the mortar, then extended both ways along the wire.

other 4400 pipes was the same except that it contained calcium chloride in concentrations from 1½ to 3 percent by weight of the cement.

Some 29 pipes of the first 84 made without calcium chloride were broken open and examined; one was totally demolished so that every inch of wire was exposed. No corrosion was found. About 58 of the pipes made with mortar containing calcium chloride were examined, and corrosion was found in every one. The conclusion that calcium chloride was to blame seemed inescapable. However, there were varied opinions as to what other conditions may have contributed (Figure 6.2). Electrical potentials between core and cover of the pipe; recirculation of curing water which caused an increase in its salt content; absence of cooling and lubricant in the wire drawing process; and stress corrosion were among the possible additional factors contributing to the failure.

Corrosion problems were revealed during construction of a huge prestressed reservoir, described below, where a different method of prestressing was used.

PRESTRESSED RESERVOIR, RICHMOND, CALIFORNIA—1955[164, 165]

This 12 million gallon water storage tank, 204 ft in diameter and 44 ft high, was circumferentially prestressed by 360 parallel-wire cables (18 wires each), encased in flexible metal sheaths, cast within the tank walls. Each cable extended over an arc of 90 deg, with its ends anchored at concrete pilasters in the wall. Cables were tensioned by pulling the ends against the pilasters with hydraulic jacks. The ends were then to be anchored against pilasters and the cable sheaths filled with grout to prevent corrosion. There were 320 cables of 18 wires each to provide vertical prestressing.

Tensioning of the cables was done in two stages after the concrete wall attained sufficient strength. Something less than the total required elongation was produced in the first stage, and in the second stage the required elongation was to be accomplished after some creep of steel and plastic flow of concrete had occurred. During second-stage pretensioning a number of the circumferential wires were found corroded and broken. The wire placed in the walls had been under stress and exposed to air and moisture about 3 months between initial stressing and discovery of the rupture.

It was decided to remove all 204 miles of wire from the metal sheaths and replace it with new wire. During the replacement operation, it was found that most of the cables had some broken wires, some had all 18 wires broken, and many wires had more than one break in their 170-ft length. When the new wires were placed and stressed, the cables were grouted immediately, and the tank has shown no signs of distress since. However, the owner discontinued use of this prestressing method.

The following spectacular collapse of a 10 year old cylindrical prestressed tank released a deluge of half-digested sludge over the grounds of the Owls Head Sewage Treatment Plant and a nearby railroad yard in New York.

PRESTRESSED SLUDGE DIGESTION TANK, NEW YORK, N.Y.—1961[166, 167]

A cylindrical prestressed concrete sludge digestion tank collapsed without warning and without witnesses, a total loss. The 103 ft diameter tank, one of a battery of eight of similar design, had 12-in. walls and a sludge depth of 36 ft. Tanks were arranged in two rows of four, along with two storage tanks and a gasholder. Sufficient walls and roof sections were added between tanks to form an enclosure for operating equipment and personnel. Roofs were conventionally reinforced slabs supported on the walls and on reinforced concrete beams and columns. There was a 30-ft gas dome above each tank at its center.

Vertical prestressing steel (0.192-in. wires) inside the tank was within chases, 24 in. on centers, covered with ⅝ in. of troweled mortar. Circumferential prestressing was by high strength wire, 0.192 inches in diameter, wrapped continuously around the exterior of the tank and tensioned to about 100,000 psi by die-drawing to 0.142-in. diameter. The horizontal wires were covered with at least ¾ in. of sprayed-on mortar. Brick facing had been applied over most of the exposed exterior, separated from the concrete tank by a 2-in. air space.

The author was retained by the public works department to investigate,* and found that the tank failure resulted from a loss in wire section to the point where there was insufficient hoop tension to withstand the liquid pressure. The wires on the outer face of the tank which had been brick covered and indirectly subject to exterior rain and temperature variation were considerably eroded and corroded, and were the immediate cause of the collapse. The major portion of the tank perimeter, however, was inside the work room where climatic conditions were favorably controlled. The wires removed from this part of the wall were also found, with few exceptions, severely rusted and with brittle cone-end fractures and longitudinal splits. Some of the wires, which for unknown reasons showed no outside rusting, when bent were also found to have corroded longitudinal splits in the

---

* More details of the investigation are reported in Reference 13.

Figure 6.3—Prestressed concrete tank used for sludge digestion collapsed suddenly at Owls Head Sewage Treatment Plant in New York in 1961. Failure was attributed to corrosion of prestressing steel, and the 10-year-old tank was a total loss. Other similar tanks (background) were strengthened with steel liners following the incident.

interior. Similar steel wires used for vertical post-tensioning, and located on the inner faces of the walls, were found in perfect shape. These wires were straight, had not been die-stressed, and were covered with mortar as part of the inside surface of the tank.

The major cause of loss of wire section seems to have been internal stress corrosion caused by electrochemical action, together with a smaller loss on the surface of the wires from electrolytic and chemical corrosion. The tanks which remained standing showed localized expansive force causing the fall of small areas of pneumatically placed concrete covering, in areas not covered by exterior brickwork, and it was recommended that interior steel liners be placed in the remaining tanks to resist the full liquid pressure.

Another investigator[168] asserted that construction details contributed to widespread corrosion difficulties. Drainage from the roof entered the cavity between brick facing and the core wall. Galvanized metal anchors for the brick facing were embedded in the mortar covering for the prestressing wires (about ¾ in. thick) in almost direct contact with the wires, instead of having a minimum of ⅝ in. mortar between dovetail and prestressing wire as present day practice would suggest. The metal anchors were corroded by roof drainage and probably provided an avenue of access for roof drainage to the prestressing steel.

For protection of prestressing steel in a corrosive environment, there must be a substantial, complete mortar or concrete coating, and detrimental cracking of the structure must be avoided by a conservative knowledgeable approach to design. Some agencies have adopted the practice of specifying a protective coating over the prestressing steel of tanks and of pipe consisting of a flash coat of neat cement slurry followed immediately by a coat of cement and sand mortar. It is believed the slurry improves the reinforcement protection by providing additional hydroxides and by minimizing voids in the coating in the vicinity of the steel. It is also necessary to avoid any stray currents being carried through the tanks into the prestressing wire.

It may be advisable that prestressed concrete tanks be treated similarly to other structures with periodic inspections to insure continued proper performance. Because of the belief that concrete is maintenance free, large apparent distress has been ignored and consequently major corrective measures have become necessary. If these problems had been detected earlier, less costly corrections could have been made.

HIGHWAY SURFACES

Another frequent item of concrete distress is the surface disintegration of pavements, curbs, and sidewalks. Whether the result of traffic action on a poorly surfaced concrete, aided by the chemical and abrasive additives to control snow coverage, the fact that there are so many good concrete surfaces of many years life, shows that some detail or combination of construction details has been improperly introduced. In 1958, the New York State Thruway Authority spent about a million dollars in the repair of concrete wearing surface on some 80 to 90 bridges. The design consisted of a 4-in. concrete wearing surface on a waterproofed bridge slab. The top slabs sometimes heaved, and in other areas just eroded. After 2 years of sad experience with the specified separate 4 in. thick wearing courses, the New York Department of Public Works modified its standards in 1959 to provide an asphaltic concrete wearing course and open grating drains to remove the brine from the direct salting for snow removal. The new standards permit a concrete surface if it is cast monolithically with the structural slab. Most of the earlier bridge decks have been resurfaced or surface sealed to protect against the chemical action of the future salting.

The concrete bridge slabs of the New Jersey Turnpike crossing the Passaic River have also required repairs costing almost a million dollars, and finally the complete removal and replacement of the concrete deck for some 4800 lane feet after only 7 years in use. In the same geographical and climatic areas, the concrete pavement of the Pulaski Highway bridges after 25 years use with very little maintenance, wore too smooth from the traffic density and required a surface coating ("retreading") to give it the necessary traction.

Before replacement of the slab on the Passaic River bridges, a complete investigation of signs of distress, physical and chemical tests of the concrete in place, and correlation between conditions of individual slabs and construction reports led to the following findings:

1. Although concrete cylinders during construction tested at 3000 psi, the cores taken at 7 years averaged only 2500 psi.

2. Concrete was more porous and less dense than anticipated.

3. Readily discernible are the variations in appearance and texture of the concrete at different locations.

4. The reinforcing steel is closer to the surface than the 1½-in. cover intended.

5. Aggregate tests and cement content more than complied with the original specifications.

6. There is no correlation between the variations in surface texture or appearance and the incidence of failure.

7. Earliest and most severe failures occurred where the bars were close to the surface, but many failures did occur where the steel was covered by 1½ in. of concrete, and damage resulted from the expansive forces of the rusting steel.

In the reconstruction, the slab thickness was increased from 6¾ to 7½ in., and the steel was covered by 1¾ in. of concrete and fixed in position by welding to tie bars, which were welded to the steel beams. Special care was taken to eliminate plastic cracking.

Production of bond-financed turnpikes is set at fast schedules to save investment costs. Sometimes the schedules are too fast for the production of a good product. Just as it takes time to make good bread, it takes time to produce good concrete. A rush job, no matter what the specifications say or how rigid the intended supervision and inspection, cannot result in good work. Perhaps the announcements of records in volume of concrete placed in a day should be replaced by more pride in the quality of the job produced.

INCOMPATIBILITY OF CONCRETE WITH OTHER MATERIALS

The incompatibility of diverse materials, whether connected or merely adjoining, shows itself in never-ending cracking and spalling, seldom leading to collapse but causing expensive maintenance and unsightly surfaces. The incompatibility stems from the variance in reaction to changing conditions of age, moisture, temperature, loading, vibration, and use. An early example of such distress is the rain absorbing separation at all contacts between timber and stucco in the Tudor facades.

Masonry Enclosure of Concrete Frames

One of the most serious difficulties of this nature is found in the masonry enclosure of concrete frames. When the masonry is a continuous surface of hard-burnt, nonshrinking brick, stone, or enameled burnt clay product, laid with tight mortar joints, no provision has been made for the future shrinkage from delayed setting and plastic flow of the concrete columns. Experience with stone facing on steel frame buildings has shown the necessity of lead relieving joints about 20 ft apart, otherwise the stone is subject to cracking and spalling. No such corrective measure is customary with brick covering and the result is often seen as spalled brick, usually near the lowest story, bowed faces with resulting open horizontal joints, and cracked brick.

The greater magnitude of shrinkage and plastic flow when lightweight concrete is used in the columns has brought a number of legal disputes between owner and contractor when the brick facing cracks and sometimes peels. The first high rise structure in New York with lightweight concrete columns was erected in 1956. Within a year of completion, the brick started to spall, especially at the second-floor level in the continuous masonry piers. Removal and replacement of some masonry only partly corrected the difficulties. The masonry remained under high compressive stress, with the facing of the brick coming off. Identical trouble has been found in several other buildings of the same design.[109]

The defect seems to be the delayed shrinkage of the concrete, throwing unusual load on the more rigid brickwork, which then buckles and spalls. The usual rapid construction schedule, with the brickwork installed in the lower floors before completion of the concrete, increases the relative compressive deformation. Plastic flow of the concrete in the columns places a high load on the reinforcement with consequent elastic shrinkage. The magnitude of the differential shrinkage need not be high to create serious distress.

Reports of the same error in attempting to combine a non-shrinking skin with shrinking columns have been received from Boston and Philadelphia. In Chicago, the problem has been avoided by making columns of standard concrete and using lightweight material for the slabs only. This combination, however, brings some construction difficulties in keeping the mixes separate and in maintaining high shear resistance in the flat plate design at the columns. A simpler remedy which has proved effective is the introduction of a caulked mastic joint under each angle lintel level, carrying the angles completely around the building perimeter.

Leakage in masonry walls is widespread among all sizes, shapes, and ages of buildings. Once the moisture has entered the wall, continuous shape changes occur and the leakage paths increase and enlarge. At the contacts between concrete and masonry, continuous membrane flashing will act to stop the moisture from entering the building. Such flashing as actually installed is seldom continuous. It is standard practice to anchor the brick facing to the concrete columns and spandrels by dovetail anchors or metal ties. These items perforate the membrane and no painting with asphalt is sufficient to seal the openings.

Shrinkage of the concrete frame may disrupt the continuity of the waterproofing. Klock and Sheridan[170] reported that a 275x131-ft factory building of the Eastman Kodak Co. in Rochester, N.Y., was carefully observed from 1939 to 1956, with shrinkage increasing over the full 16-year period. The total then measured for the seven-story flat slab structure was 0.0985 percent vertically and 0.0460 percent horizontally. In a 200 ft high concrete frame, not uncommon for an apartment or office building, the vertical shrinkage is about 2½ in. To this should be added the elastic compression from the loading contributed by the wall and the interior finish and live loads, which will be about the same as the compression of the brickwork unless relieving joints are provided. As the concrete shrinks, the masonry face becomes a free standing sheet. If the masonry is supported on steel lintel angles, localized compression is found in the courses just below the angles. If continuously laid up, broken and spalled brick will be found at points some 100 ft from the top and below such elevation. The difficulty of course is compounded by thermal changes, the range being much greater for the covering than it is for the frame.

Back-up masonry for stone facing must be substantially as rigid as the facing. Use of soft brick or tile blocks for backing natural stone or precast concrete units always leads to trouble. This is true whether the wall panels are solid or of cavity construction.

Cavity walls built of dissimilar materials in the two wythes should be investigated for the load bearing capacity and stability of the more rigid wythe to carry the entire load, usually eccentrically located on the support. Rotation of the carrying lintel angle will cause bulges and horizontal cracks in the face. In some cases, hold back angles are necessary near the top of the story height to prevent the front wythe falling out. Anchorage to a less rigid inner wythe is no structural safeguard against rotation.

Volume Change and Vibration

Plastic flow of concrete in long spans where a hard floor finish has been applied will cause the finish to loosen since the shrinkage of the more rigid and more carefully applied topping is less than of normal concrete. Vibration will aid in this separation, as is noted by the poor condition of most terrazzo finishes near elevator and escalator openings.

Vibration from rail traffic has caused high maintenance of tile surfacing in the New York subway stations. The oldest stations did not have tile extending from floor to roof; either the top of the tile was left free entirely or else butted against a plaster strip. When the tile surfacing of a number of station extensions was carried tight to the roof construction, the transfer of vibrations into the rigidly held skin caused cracking almost immediately. Replacement of the cracked tile under a 5-year guarantee called for by the contract, made three times in that period, was of no avail.

Mortar surfacing on concrete is seldom successful, due to differences in shrinkage and in thermal reaction. In European and in South American practice the surfacing is applied in three coats, the first being a slaked lime mortar, the next a blend of lime and cement and the top surface of practically all cement to give the waterproof skin. Even with the more flexible inner layers, and the high humidities in these areas, such surfacing has been observed to crack and craze after 10 years, even where installed by the most experienced craftsmen.

DELAYED SHRINKAGE

Certain types of lightweight aggregate concrete blocks shrink badly at an age of one to two years. Where used for filling in panels between brick, concrete, or steel piers, the shrinkage is large enough to cause cracks through which daylight penetrates. In two modern school buildings on Long Island, the shrinkage was so serious that drafts were noticeable within the building and complete stucco covering was necessary. As an opposite type of behavior, a motel built with concrete slab roofs cast into the top course of masonry blocks forming the cross walls required considerable reconstruction when the 200 ft long slabs shrank at an age of about 6 months and pulled the masonry blocks apart. This condition existed in the outer quarter lengths of the construction, the displacement increasing towards the ends. A similar design in Yonkers, N.Y., where the slab was placed on a waterproof paper separation placed on top of the block walls (these buildings also over 200 ft long) showed no interaction, although there are signs of shrinkage separations between the slabs and the end walls.

MAGNESIA CEMENTS

The expansive action of magnesia cements in the presence of moisture has resulted in the popping out of sections near ventilation grilles in hung ceilings where the mortar had an abnormal magnesia content. The metal lath being of more stable dimension, the plaster separated and fell. Two large shopping centers of identical design in the Washington area were constructed of the same materials except for the type of mortar for the plaster. The one with high magnesia content failed; the other showed no distress. Failure started at an age of about 18 months, during the second cooling season for the air conditioning equipment.

Plaster and Paint Surfacing

Application of plaster or paint on concrete surfaces for interior finish has been a troublesome item. For many years after direct application of finish plaster on concrete ceilings became an acceptable practice, a patented gypsum product was sold with guarantee of adhesion. But so many claims for noncompliance arose that the product was taken off the market. Plastic spray coatings were then developed to act as bonding agent between concrete and white plaster. Although very successful in most instances, the permanence depending upon a continuous supply of moisture vapor to maintain a colloidal gel, there have been a number of failures in air-conditioned buildings, apparently from the dehydration of the concrete and of the plaster.

In low rental subsidized housing, and in many private apartment structures, direct painting on the concrete is considered sufficient. However, the compatibility of coating materials with concrete surfaces requires careful study before writing into the specifications new or untried combinations. In a large development in Detroit and in some similar designs in the eastern cities, it was found impossible to spread the paint onto the concrete. The paint became gummy and rolled into threads. Investigation showed that in each case a new pressed-board form had been used and the concrete had absorbed some resinous compound from the form. The paint dissolved the resin and became gummy. A report on this investigation was published in 1948.[171]

Aluminum

Direct contact between aluminum and cement must be avoided because of corrosive staining. Nonreactive protective coatings on aluminum mullions and other fixtures may overcome this difficulty.

During the steel strike in 1959, several buildings in New York substituted aluminum conduit for the conventional steel item but continued use of steel outlet and junction boxes. All of these buildings are now showing distress, with cracked ceilings outlining all conduit runs. In one building with an integral terrazzo floor, the finished floor is cracking and heaving. The aluminum conduit, from chemical action with the cement and stray electric current electrolysis, disintegrates into an oxide with expansive forces causing the cracking and spalling.

The Department of Licenses and Inspections of the District of Columbia has reported considerable cracking in slabs along runs of embedded aluminum conduit. Use of aluminum conduit within concrete was prohibited in 1963 by the General Services Administration of the federal government, and is losing its popularity elsewhere. Recent reports indicate that the U.S. Army Corps of Engineers and the Public Buildings Service (federal) have also banned the use of aluminum conduits in concrete.[172]

In the failure of the prestressed tanks described on p. 126, it was noted that the aluminum torpedo-shaped connectors used to splice the steel wires had completely disintegrated. Chemical analysis of the white powder found in the cavity showed it to be pure aluminum oxide. Tests for stray electric currents were negative; the change was purely a contact phenomenon between aluminum and cement, in a conductor made of two metals. A white powdery compound was also found on aluminum conduit embedded at points of spalling of concrete members in a Washington, D.C., stadium.[172]

7

Foundation Problems;
Special Types of Structures

THERE ARE FEW RECORDED FAILURES of foundations as a structural unit.
One exception, which occurred in 1895, caused the collapse of the
eight-story Ireland Building, an early New York skyscraper, just as
the roof was being completed.[173] The design was a system of concrete
floors between iron beams of 25-ft span, supported by the exterior
walls and a single line of cast iron columns. The second interior
column punched through the footing which was found to have one
corner built directly over an old well. The concrete had filled the well
completely but most of the footing was on fine wet silt. The footing
tipped and the entire rear part of the building fell into the cellar.
Other exceptions are the punching of a stone footing by a cast iron
column at the old Chicago Club building;[174] the crushing of the
foundation which caused the failure of the Barentin Viaduct near
Havre, France; and the crushing of the lime concrete foundations of
the concrete engine shed on the British Metropolitan Railway, which
caused a complete collapse of the shed.[175] All these structures were
built before 1900, but the Chicago Club failure did not occur until
remodeling was under way in 1928.

Much more common than the crushing or collapse of a footing or
other foundation member is the unequal settlement of such units
caused by changing subgrade conditions or by a wrong assumption

in the foundation design. Foundation designs are often based on widely separated test borings. During excavation and construction, the engineer should be at hand to check and confirm the assumptions on which he based his design. If unexpected subgrade conditions are found, he should be ready to modify the foundation design. Unanticipated subgrade conditions have been the cause of failures where footings were actually left suspended in soil without any bearing. Instead of providing support, the footing and the column above it acted in reverse, increasing the loads in surrounding bays and columns.

Because structural continuity almost always exists in concrete structures, they are particularly vulnerable to damage from foundation deficiency. Even partial loss of one support causes radical revision of moment and shear stresses in a continuous structure. Seldom is a structure designed for such a condition. Exceptions are continuous bridges and decking structures to support street loading over subway and similar excavations. Typical custom in designing decking for New York subway construction, where main beams are carried over several supports, some of which may accidentally be displaced or clearance requirements make it mandatory to move one support at a time, is to

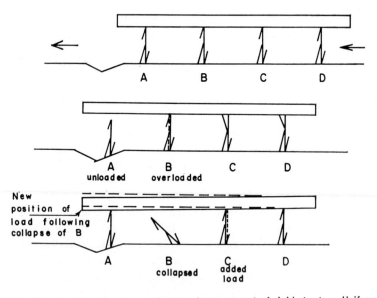

Figure 7.1—Load transfer from settlement of one support of rigid structure. Uniform reactions at A, B, C, and D are modified if Man A steps into a depression or soft spot. B is then overloaded and may collapse, throwing load back on A as shown in bottom sketch.

permit normal stresses with all supports in place and survival stresses with any one support removed. To follow such procedure in all structures would considerably increase construction costs. It is therefore important to provide uniformly consolidating supports for all columns of a concrete structure.

In 1940 at the Purdue University conference on soil mechanics, the author showed some sketches to explain sudden changes in bracing reactions in trench sheeting. The same explanation is repeated here because it applies to several types of structural frame failure where unexpected loads and reactions occur. A rigid beam (Figure 7. 1) carried by four men who have located themselves so as to support equal loads is being carried along a smooth surface. When Man A steps into a depression, Man B is overloaded and may collapse, throwing the load back to A and some additional load to C, with possible uplift on D. This simple qualitative description of the change in reactions of a continuous structure when one support is displaced explains many types of structural failures. Many failures due to gravity result from an earlier lateral displacement along a contact where uplift is not resisted.

INADEQUATE OR UNEQUAL SUPPORT FOR FOUNDATIONS

In 1904, a 13-story framed apartment building in New York City failed completely when the steel work was at the tenth floor and the concrete floors were being installed on the seventh floor.[176] The front wall was supported on square cast iron columns carrying loadings with 12 in. eccentricity and with footings founded on rock. The rear of the building was on clay soil with some quicksand. The framework started to sway towards the street, reversed itself and fell into the lot. The loss of 25 workmen caused a detailed investigation, but the lesson was not learned, nor did the failure prevent later repetition of the same mistakes—eccentric loading on cast iron columns and unequal soil bearing values within a single structure.

Good foundations are often ruined as a load carrying element by unexpected subsurface conditions similar to the case of the Ireland Building collapse in New York. A 1907 report by Paul Sée[177] cited the sudden tipping of a 6 year old brick chimney 80 ft high on a large concrete base. Investigation showed a hollow under the base, about 100 cu yd in volume. Small flow of ground water to an abandoned well about 50 ft away had carried the fine sand away from under the footing, unnoticed until collapse almost occurred. A similar condition was described by Sée at a two-story building in Spain where a buried water course robbed the soil from the center of the building causing continuous settlement of the middle of the structure with the ends remaining stable.

A well publicized collapse of a four-story flat slab concrete structure in 1953 in Westchester County, N.Y.,* during the placing of concrete in the fourth floor slab was diagnosed on the basis of personal observation and photographs which all showed a characteristic funnel shaped debris pattern. It has been found in the investigations of several collapses, that the debris leaves such a funnel and that the axis of the funnel points towards the first movement. The axis pointed towards one column. In addition, it was found that a plywood scale model of the portions which had collapsed on all the floors, when suspended upside down, balanced at the same column. Later investigation, after removal of the debris, showed that this column in the bottom story was tipped toward the exterior wall and the foundation conditions under the exterior wall columns were not the sound rock called for on the design plans. Transfer of load, in this case the weight of the concrete alone, caused overstress at foundation level, tipping and loss of support in the flat slab floors. The slab could not span 54 ft, after one support became inoperative, and so collapse resulted.

The investigation showed several other defects which contributed to the seriousness of the collapse, and the structure was almost completely demolished before reconstruction, but only after some 40 column footings were reinforced or enlarged. First publicity on this collapse placed the blame on form support failure; by the time the facts were available, this matter no longer was considered news. Lack of control and inspection of the foundation work cost everyone concerned tremendous sums of money, not to mention the loss of three lives and injury to other workmen.

Some spectacular failures of structures due to poor foundation planning have been reported from Brazil in recent years (see also p. 143). In February, 1946, a nearly completed 10-story apartment building in Rio de Janeiro collapsed, killing 14 workers.[178] On the day of the collapse, the head of the construction firm was shown a crack in a second-floor column. He ordered a temporary wooden prop placed while he went out to get patching material, without ordering workers out of the structure. By the time he had returned, the building was a heap of rubble. Generally shoddy work stimulated by a speculative building boom at the time was blamed for the collapse, but investiga-

---

* This incident is described more fully on p. 71, because of additional defects which contributed to the wide extent of the collapse.

tion brought out the fact that site examination a year earlier disclosed an underground stream 5 m below the surface. Pumping had been done, but no piles were driven.

When the 11-story Rua Rosario building collapsed in 1957 only thirty minutes after a city engineer declared it safe,[179] the Rio papers started a storm of complaint and investigation.[180] The magazine, *O Cruzeiro* listed 20 buildings which collapsed in the past 10 years and ran pictures of buildings on the main avenues which were 8 to 12 in. out of plumb. The Rua Rosario building failure was triggered by the pumping of water and soil by an adjacent construction. This type of foundation failure is well documented, and proper precautions can be taken and should be considered a part of the design.

SOIL AND GROUND WATER MOVEMENTS

Several comparatively new dwellings in the St. Louis area recently became unsafe and uninhabitable because of movement of the loess soil on which they were built (Figure 7.2). Natural slope of the building lots was about 1 to 11, front to rear, and no difficulty was experienced with initial fill terraces up to 7 ft high with a finished slope of 1 to 3. However, later cutting and grading outside the rear lot lines to a depth of 10 ft, also on a slope of 1 to 3, led to a slide in the wet season of 1956. Several houses were damaged beyond hope of repair, and movement of the slide continued intermittently for about 4 years. The problem resulted from having too great a height for the slope inclination and for the strength of the underlying soil.[181]

Figure 7.2—Homes in a St. Louis area subdivision looked like this as a result of soil slides which removed foundation support, leaving a number of relatively new dwellings uninhabitable.

Variation in ground water levels may seriously alter the supporting value of the soils and cause major damage or collapse of the structure. A drop in subsurface water level at Elk Point, S.D., in 1956 caused soil dessication and weakening with damage to almost every building.[182] A buckling wall forced evacuation of the high school; cracks appeared in all masonry bearing walls and the extent of the damage exceeded a million dollars in repairs. Some of the older European cities, such as Amsterdam, where a lowering of the ground water would imperil the safety of the wood pile foundations have arranged protection by maintaining a fixed water table level.

The drought of 1952-53 in the Kansas City area caused structural damage to perhaps as many as 65 percent of all the homes. The estimated potential repair bill was in the order of $20 to 40 million, which would have been saved if some water level control had been provided to prevent soil dessication.

Fluctuating water levels over a period of 15 years weakened the shale under the Peace River Bridge of the Alcan Highway in British Columbia, and the north abutment slid 12 ft riverward in 1957 with the result that the bridge was abandoned and replaced.[183]

Expanding Soils

Expanding shales and clays cause large damage to structures built thereon. The Housing and Home Finance Agency has issued a number of reports and bulletins to advise the home owner how to protect the investment against soil movements caused by alternate wetting and drying. Localized trouble of this nature occurs where poplar and similar trees act as moisture removers along side walls. The effect of a large poplar can be noted as far as 35 ft from the trunk. The safest procedure is to found the buildings on cored piles.

A major structure, the $1.5 million Justice Building in Little Rock, displayed buckling and cracking of walls, floors, and ceilings when it was less than four years old in 1960.[184] The building was erected on high-porosity clay which reportedly heaved and dropped as its moisture content varied. According to the architect, "lack of funds" made necessary the omission of proper footings that could have prevented the trouble.

Recent development of suburban Cleveland indicates a new source of soil volume change as a cause of structural distress. A belt running eastward from Cleveland along the shores of Lake Erie has a soil with sufficient iron pyrites which when exposed to dampness for a long period will oxidize and the pyrite crystals expand to ten times their original volume. Exposure of the shales containing the pyrites is now immediately sprayed with bitumen to prevent oxidation. Where this precaution has not been taken, walls, floors, and lightly loaded footings have heaved and cracked.

Checking and confirming of design assumptions as construction proceeded—the practice recommended on p. 136—forestalled failure of a 30 million gal. reservoir near Denver in 1960.[185] A shale formation, which swelled as much as 4 in. when exposed to heavy rains during excavation indicated that the originally planned 8-in. reinforced slab placed on compacted material would be unsatisfactory. The redesign of the reservoir floor provided for a system of thin shell concrete barrel arches supported on drilled cast-in-place caissons at a cost increase of about $500,000. The flat, continuous barrel shells had a rise of only 1 ft 10 in. in 10 ft, and cleared the ground by a minimum of 18 in. Water depth in the reservoir was 24 ft.

FROST ACTION

The formation of growing ice crystals, exerting pressures of several tons per sq ft, is a cause of many troubles. The continually expanding cracks exposed to water during below-freezing temperatures produce surface cracking and spalling of roads and walls regardless of the construction material. Frost penetration of the subgrade on which concrete footings are placed will heave the footings if moisture is available to form ice crystals. Spring thaws will bring settlements of the structure.

An interesting situation of this nature occurred in Watertown, N.Y., an area of very cold winters. Footings and piers to grade for an apartment house were completed in the fall and the work was backfilled and left for the winter. With the next construction season, the timber sills and framing were set on the piers and work was well advanced when considerable distortion was observed. A study of conditions showed that the frost action in the fill around the piers had lifted the piers off the footings as much as 12 in., and had held the supports during the construction work until the ground thawed. Repair work required the exposure of all piers, grouting solid to the footings and a re-leveling of the entire floor construction. Similar upheaval of concrete block walls backfilled to grade and left during a winter in Detroit, in 1938, was observed when work started again.

Another serious frost damage occurred in a substructure contract where completed piers with anchor bolts embedded were left exposed during the winter. Bolts had been placed in oversize sleeves to permit some adjustment to fit steel base plates. Water filled the sleeves, froze, and cracked off the edges of many piers. Such open sleeves, even if only for future railings, should be covered or filled with nonfreezing materials.

PILE FOUNDATIONS

It is impossible in a monograph of this sort to give comprehensive coverage to the structural problems stemming from pile foundation difficulties. A few cases are cited, merely to show the range of problems.

Prevention of possible failure was the subject of an interdepartmental bulletin, May 18, 1960, of the Western Electric Company:

> "Since the driving of the foundation piles for the six-story Bell Telephone Laboratories' project at Holmdel and the adding of concrete caps to many of the clusters of piles, a possibility has arisen that there might be undesirable settlement in some of the clusters. This possibility arose when comparing driving results for test piles driven before and after many of the clusters were driven. To prevent undesirable settlement occurring as the building is constructed and after its completion, a program of preloading most of the clusters to their full ultimate load and then removing the load is being undertaken this week. In this way, the full settlement of the ultimate loads, which have in them estimates of loading due to laboratory operations that may never be realized, will be obtained in advance of building. If, for any reason, the preloading should indicate an unsatisfactory condition, the particular cluster involved will be re-engineered and rebuilt.
>
> "Some of the clusters are too large and too complicated to preload. Hence, their caps, if they have already been capped, will be removed and the individual piles will be checked. The piles in clusters which have not been capped will be driven a short distance to insure that they have not lost their bearing since the original driving and will be supplemented by additional piles if necessary. This program will preclude any future possibility of excessive settlement."

Such an expenditure of funds and delay in construction program is most unusual and indicates the acceptance of the proposition that a good building deserves a good foundation. But one wonders why the problem was not solved earlier.

A contrasting example of what can happen if no one suspects or finds a foundation deficiency, is the case of the five-story concrete office building near Montreal, P.Q. This fine looking brick encased structure, founded on piles of large capacity, was almost completed, when, over the Labor Day weekend in 1958, it tilted suddenly 10 in. from level in the length of about 200 ft. Emergency jacking with steel piles arrested further movement and painful exposure of the intrusion-type piles indicated the trouble. Too rapid a withdrawal of the casing as the concrete was forced into position permitted lenses of mud to intrude and create discontinuities in the pile shafts. The reduced carrying capacity permitted crushing. Rapid successive failure of the cylinders as load was transferred by the previous failures, all without warning, caused settlement of the building.

Thorough inspection of the settled structure failed to indicate a single item of distress in any of its members. Yet, no acceptable method of correcting the sloping position could be devised, and so the building was demolished and rebuilt on new piers. The possibility of mud intrusion that would again make them discontinuous was eliminated by providing permanent steel casings. With the history of thousands of successful installations of such piers, it seems that the omission of that one precautionary detail in the original piers had been a serious and expensive mistake.

By a strange accident, an equally serious condition was discovered at the LaGuardia Airport Building (New York) in 1961.[157]

A small revision in plan required the shortening of some piles so that fuel tanks could be buried. When the piles were cut down, some of the steel shells were found to have voids in the concrete filling. A random sampling of piles was drilled, and when found suspect as indicated by nonuniform drill resistance and a change in the color of the dust, core samples were also taken. Sufficient piles were found improperly filled—two had voids over 30 ft long—to warrant a complete rejection of the completed pile job. Concrete caps were removed, new piles driven, and the work delayed about a year. When some of the suspect piles were withdrawn, the coring record was found to indicate correctly the continuity, density, and mix deficiencies of the concrete within the pile shell.

Just how this concreting was so poorly performed, in spite of experienced crews and inspection personnel, is hard to explain. It makes one wonder how many such conditions exist as undiscovered threats to structural stability.

A different type of pile deficiency was responsible when the 11-story Sao Luis Rei building in Rio de Janeiro failed by overturning Jan. 30, 1958.[186] The 95x39-ft structure was supported on 99 concrete piles 69 ft long. The site was an old quagmire, and other buildings in the area had 86-ft piles. Differential settlement caused by the too-short piles had been noticed as early as April, 1956, when construction crews were at the tenth floor. In January, 1957, a second rather violent movement occurred, but both of these were described by the engineers as "natural settlement." There was little indication of further movement until January 24, 1958, when the building appeared to be settling badly at the long rear side. Underpinning operations were started on a round-the-clock basis, but too late to save the rotating building. The settlement rate increased, and the whole building tipped dizzily to the rear and fell flat January 30.

RETAINING WALLS AND ABUTMENTS

Failures of retaining walls have been so common in the past that little publicity is given to the incidents unless some spectacular damage or loss of life is involved. Retaining wall failures are still too common; evidently copying standard designs without allowance for the possible change in soil conditions and acting pressures is not sufficient. Statistics offer a clue to the probable cause; most failures in the New York area occur within days after the usual warm spring rains. Examination of many of these incidents shows the usual additional pressure comes from the action of ice forming in cavities in back of and under the wall structure, water pressure from the filling of continuous voids, and the wedging action of expanding tree trunks and roots, especially the Chinese sumac and in one case climber rose. Perhaps Robert Frost was right when he said in the poem "East of Boston," "Something there is that doesn't love a wall, that wants it down."

Failure to follow design and detail can cause wall failures unless errors are caught in time, as described in two cases from the author's records. One was a buttress type retaining wall where the foreman insisted that the horizontal bars shown on the drawings bent over the supporting buttress should be cut and hooked into the buttress. The bars had come to the job prefabricated and correct. This wall was to provide support for a railroad siding. It required a call from the railroad bridge engineer, with the threat that no siding track would be built, to get the reinforcement corrected. The second case concerned a retaining wall of cantilever type (p. 67). The footing had been built, the dowels for the stem were being bent out of position, and the reinforcement for the wall proper was being placed along the front or exposed face when a routine inspection stopped the work. The foreman insisted that the plan was wrong.

Reports of the collapse of an ornamental reinforced brick wall at a school in Houston, Tex., in 1959 showed that the failure of the 8 ft high wall which killed a schoolgirl resulted from improper spacing and the reduction of length of the bars from that shown on the design drawings.*

Carefully prepared designs and details are necessary for retaining walls, and as indicated by the foregoing cases as well as the Manhasset wall where ¼-in. bars replaced the 1¼-in. steel shown in the design, experienced supervision is necessary to get compliance with the designer's ideas. With good design, carefully executed, failures could then be limited to the cases where conditions change with time, for example, the failure of the bridge pier in 1905 in Arizona when a normally small stream went into flood, running at 12 miles per hour. The entire space under the pier was washed out causing 30 ft long piles to fail, and two 200-ft bridge spans fell into the stream bed.[187]

Large projects are not immune to wall failure as was illustrated by the rotation of the retaining wall along the Union Pacific Railroad yard at Portland, Ore., in 1958.[188] The wall was a maximum of 70 ft high and had just been completed when 240 ft collapsed, requiring the excavation of 165,000 cu yd of displaced fill and reconstruction of 1000 ft of street pavement retained by the wall.

Liquid Pressure

Change in the pressures to be sustained by walls often occurs when fine grained backfill becomes liquid when saturated. In a housing development in Hartford, Conn. in 1939, where concrete cellar walls were backfilled with the local clay soils, a heavy storm running down the contoured garden areas changed the fills to a liquid mud and caused the complete collapse of several walls. After reconstruction, the lesson was not learned and the same backfill materials used. A second similar storm resulted in the same action, and some of the reconstructed walls failed a second time. Backfilling thereafter was done with granular materials.

Walls designed for full or partly balanced pressure, such as the dividing wall in the coagulation basin of the Baltimore water filtration plant must be guarded against being required to sustain full pressure from one side. When one basin was emptied in 1929, with the adjacent one remaining full, the separation wall was undermined by the flow of water through small cavities; the base pressures were altered and the entire wall with its base and shear key moved out bodily, releasing

---

* "Short Bars Blamed for Brick Wall Collapse," *Engineering News-Record*, V. 162, No. 24, June 18, 1959, p. 48.

some 8 million gal. of water.[189] Actually a wall section 240 ft long was floated away, parts moving 60 ft. Testimony of responsible men in charge of the original construction was that the wall had been founded on stiff clay and rotten rock. Flowing water is known to cause such materials to soften and disintegrate.

Metamorphic rocks of the nature of schists soften under load with aging, there being a complete change in structure of the grain contacts and flow of water will form weak slip surfaces.

Sheeting

Failure of temporary sheeting walls in construction jobs is also a common occurrence, not so often from poor structural design as from lack of proper supports for the reactions from the sheeting. Loss of ground from excessive movement of the sheeting will affect adjacent structures and has been the cause of much litigation. Properly designed sheeting and bracing, properly installed is one of the best investments in a construction program. Not only does it permit maintaining schedules, but it eliminates costly legal entanglements with the neighboring owners and improves labor efficiency on the work.

Abutments

Concrete bridge abutments should not be built monolithic with their wing walls. Substantially unequal base pressures, which develop because the wing walls receive no live loadings, cause unsightly separations and sometimes tipping. It is best to consider the abutment as one structure and the wing walls as adjacent but separated retaining walls.

Differential settlement of abutments carrying simple span bridges can be compensated by wedging, as happened in the 303-ft span carrying the New York, New Haven and Hartford Railroad tracks over the Connecticut Turnpike. Because of much softer soil conditions at one side, the east abutment settled 17 in. A special design was incorporated to permit periodic jacking of the deck to maintain proper profile. In continuous bridge structures, small differential settlements of one foundation will completely alter the stress pattern and may cause serious structural distress.

The installation of jacks to correct for continuous settlement has proved successful, as in the bleachers structure of the Polo Grounds (New York) and in part of the main stand of the Yankee Stadium. However, such procedures can only serve the desired use if carefully controlled and permanently maintained. Any deviation from this rule will result in local distress and possible complete failure. With the knowledge available for proper foundation design, the additional initial expenditure for stable foundations of walls and abutments seems a wise investment.

Walls must be given freedom to move when backfilled and also when localized overpressures occur. A well-designed 20 ft high wall enclosure of a school yard in New York City has expansion joints located 20 ft apart, poorly designed for the curved lot line. The deflection of the wall sections resulted in arching strains over the upper half of the walls, and the concrete spalled along each expansion joint. In curved walls, the joints must be widened to provide clearance after deflection.

TANKS AND BINS

Tanks and silos seem to be a vulnerable type of structure; failures from many causes are reported. The failure of steel tanks for oil storage in cold weather was described by the author,[190] and Mather[191] in a discussion of the same paper cited references to 60 or 70 additional tank failures.

Large diameter concrete tanks, now usually strengthened by prestressed wire enclosures, were formerly often plagued by unusual cracking. A very early example[192] is a gas tank built in England in 1875. The concrete tank was 184 ft in diameter and 50 ft high, of which 42 ft were below ground. It was tested by filling with 35 ft of water and found without a flaw. However, when partly filled with cold water in December, cracks formed extending nearly to the bottom, probably from sudden shrinkage. Other failures of nonprestressed tanks are discussed on p. 43. Failure of tensioned wires in prestressed tanks has been reported at a number of installations, such as the Richmond reservoir described on p. 125, and in the sludge digestion tank in New York (p. 126). Monfore and Verbeck[163] indicate additional cases of difficulty with prestressing steel for tanks.

Tank Floors

Concrete reservoirs and swimming pools are prone to fail by cracking of the floor when sudden emptying does not relieve the hydrostatic pressure under the floor. In soils which do not drain rapidly, special leaching provisions are necessary to relieve the hydrostatic pressure. In some private pools where mud came up at the floor joints at every emptying, the soil being a clay, short lengths of perforated pipe were jacked under the floor from the bottom of pits excavated along the wall, and the pits were connected to a sump for relief of the upward pressures.

Mensch[44] has also pointed out the necessity for special design features at the bottom of tanks and bins where ring deformations are not compatible with the restraint of the floor.

Grain Storage Bins

Failures of concrete storage bins have been well documented. A reinforced concrete grain elevator at Duluth, Minn., had the distinction of failing twice,[193] first December 17, 1900, and again on April 16, 1903. The structure consisted of 15 circular bins, 33½ ft in diameter and 104 ft high. These cylinders were spaced so as to have 6-ft straight connection walls between them, forming a series of intermediate bins. Walls were 12 in. thick at the bottom and 9 in. at the top, reinforced with hoops made of ⅜x1½-in. steel bars spaced from 12 to 18 in. apart vertically. Both failures occurred in the same way; an intermediate bin was being filled with the adjoining circular bins empty

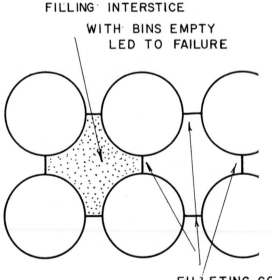

FILLING INTERSTICE
WITH BINS EMPTY
LED TO FAILURE

FILLETING CORNERS
WOULD HAVE
INCREASED STRENGTH

Figure 7.3—Cylindrical bins at Duluth elevator were arranged like this. Normal filling of circular bins places walls in hoop tension. However, when interstice was filled with bins empty, there was arch action of cylinder walls, bending in flat sides, and collapse followed.

(Figure 7.3). Walls of the circular bins split vertically almost full height; they were not strong enough to act as arches under a load of grain in the intermediate bin only, and failed to provide for bending stress at the junction between cylindrical and straight walls.

Failures of this type are due to design deficiency as pointed out by Vandegrift.[45] The cylindrical bins are normally in direct hoop tension when filled with grain, but filling the interstice with the cylinders empty produces arch action in the cylindrical walls and bending in any flat sides (straight walls of interstice). This bending is then transmitted into the cylinder walls as well. The straight walls should be designed for bending inside and outside, and corners should be filleted and properly reinforced for moment with well-anchored bars of appropriate area.

Foundation difficulties, aggravated by heavy, shifting, and unbalanced loads, are also a common cause of grain bin failures. In 1914, some Canadian Pacific Railroad bins tilted to an angle of 27 deg, and the successful righting of the structure is a classic of engineering talent. This structure was supported on a 77x195-ft concrete mat. When 85 percent loaded—at a total soil pressure of about 6100 psf—it first dropped vertically 12 in., then began to tip slowly about its long axis. After 24 hours of gradual movement, it came to rest as a unit 27 deg away from the vertical. It was righted by underpinning with open caissons to rock.[194]

More recently mudjacking was used to save a grain elevator at Lincoln, Nebr., in 1955. The 5 million bushel elevator settled 8½ in. at one end of its 273-ft length soon after completion. Test borings indicated a poor soil had resulted from underground seepage from a sandstone ledge.[195]

Less fortunate was the elevator structure at Fargo, N.D. (Figure 7.4), which failed completely, without warning and without witnesses, June 12, 1955.[196] Less than a year old, it consisted of 20 circular silos 19 ft in diameter, 120 ft high, covering an area of 52x216 ft. The foundation was made of interlocked sheet piles around the edge of this area, topped with a 30-in. concrete slab. There had been some settlement before collapse, but not enough to worry the owner. When it moved a little to the north or south "we would shift the grain," he said, "as is done in other elevators to correct the listing." Apparently the underlying soil shifted, the elevator tilted, and excess longitudinal tensile stress was induced in the walls. The lower part of the silos broke into about 15 ft lengths and the upper part shattered completely when it hit the ground.

A true explosion failure occurred in a Philadelphia grain storage elevator Mar. 28, 1956.[197] Part of the building was 90 years old, with subsequent additions of various types of construction. Although large damage was caused to wood, masonry, and steel components of the structure, as well as to windows in adjoining buildings, most of the concrete silos filled with grain suffered only superficial damage.

In 1959, one-third of a 100x375-ft elevator structure, 115 ft high, collapsed in Port Arthur, Ontario. Although it was 30 years old and founded on fill contained by a Wakefield sheet pile enclosure, repairs had not been required until 1958. At that time, some 500 cu yd of lost

Figure 7.4—An 800,000-bu grain elevator, less than one year old, collapsed at Fargo, North Dakota, in 1955, apparently following a shift of the underlying soil. The lower part of the silos broke at about the 15-ft level, and the upper part shattered when it hit the ground.

fill was replaced and 250 ft of dock wall sheet piling was added on the water side. This added protection was not sufficient to stop further soil movement which brought on the collapse the following year.

DAM FOUNDATIONS

No attempt is made here to cover the entire field of dam failures,* but only to indicate some examples of concrete structures which have failed not because of the kind of material or the nature of the struc-

---

* An informative description of 18 notable dam failures from 1880 to 1928, date of the St. Francis Dam catastrophe, was published in *Engineering News-Record*, Mar. 22, 1928. Another summary of interest is Lars Jorgensen's "Record of 100 Dam Failures," published in *Journal of Electricity* (San Francisco), Apr. 1, 1920.

tural design but because of either unexpected external loadings or loss of foundation resistance.

Dams have failed with tremendous damage and with the central section remaining intact. In 1928, the wings of the 205-ft concrete gravity St. Francis Dam some 45 miles north of Los Angeles broke away from the massive center and caused the flooding of the densely populated valley. Failure originated in the rock of one of the abutments, not in the masonry dam. In 1926 similar failure of the abutments for two thin concrete arch dams, the Moyie River Dam, Idaho, of 53 ft maximum height and the Lake Lanier Dam, Tryon, N.C., 62 ft high, caused loss of the reservoirs. In each case only one abutment washed out and the concrete dams were salvaged by adding piers to fill the gaps. Also in both dams, the bedrock foundation under load and water seepage did not remain the solid material first exposed during construction.

Dams have also failed by undermining of the main section accompanied by damage to the abutments. A most notable recent example is the Malpasset arch dam near the French Riviera, which failed in 1959. Almost 200 ft high, this dam was a product of the best design talent. Shifting of some rock formations under the left bank foundations completely voided the design assumptions. Whether the thin clay seams that would alter with pressure and presence of water could be found by more extensive boring studies is an open argument. It might be better to question the validity of any assumption of the nonexistence of seams in rock formations.

WATER FLOW

Failure of dams by overtopping, with large masonry volumes literally floating away, is a danger common to steep terrains with flash floods. In 1959, overflow from the 112-ft concreted Vega de Tera Dam in northwest Spain destroyed a village 3 miles away. Concrete spillways and covering of river revetments will float away when overtopped. Heavy spring runoff waters breached a 38-ft concrete faced spillway near Forestburg, Alberta, in 1956 and washed away 3000 cu yd of reinforced concrete and much greater quantities of earth fill.

Flooding of bridge abutments and often the sudden drop of water level causing temporary unbalanced hydrostatic pressure will displace the support, as happened in 1959 at Massena, N.Y. A canal bank caved in when water was very low and brought down a 50-ft bridge span. The bridge had served 52 years but the water level had dropped 10 ft below normal and a hard freeze possibly aided in pushing the bank into the canal.

One of the spectacular failures from water seepage through rock was the slide carrying the Schoellkopf power plant into the Niagara gorge in 1956. Following a slight earth tremor, cracks developed in the rock cliff and seepage lubricated a surface on which slid 50,000 tons of rock and about two-thirds of the power plant, causing a loss of $100 million and complete abandonment of the station. Replacement cost plus the 5-year loss of power were the results of saving a small investment in ground water seepage control.

8

Professional and Legal Responsibilities in the Prevention of Failures

MANY A STRUCTURE must pass through a critical stage during construction before the engineer can be satisfied that it is stable and a successful performance of his design. Such critical "operational shock" always requires special watching in tunnel excavations, in bridge erection, underpinnings, and concrete falsework. Failures resulting not from insufficiencies of the structural design of the completed work but from unexpected movements and loadings during construction, are, in the public mind, not distinguished from structural design failures. Published accounts of such incidents indicate that they frequently occur near the end of a job when progress is at the maximum scheduled rate and manpower is not sufficient to provide all the necessary precautions against failure. Even if the manpower is sufficient, the work is often so concentrated that space is not available for proper performance. The forces which cause these failures are not of the same magnitude or even direction as assumed loads used for structural design; simultaneously, the fresh concrete, unbraced steel, or blasted rock faces and roofs have strengths lower than the desired values as assumed by the designers.

Failures in completed structures are much less common now than when steel bridges were being sold by nontechnical salesmen on open competition, or when much less was known about concrete. The majority of failures in completed structures today result from dishonest performance and noncompliance due to ignorance, rather than from improper design.

CHANGES IN LEGAL INTERPRETATIONS

Wherein lies the responsibility when a failure occurs? Most of this text has been devoted to an exploration of the reasons for failures, but the realm of legal liability is another dimension of the problem that has to be considered. Within the past few years, increasing responsibility has been placed upon the man who acts as the prime contractor with the owner—usually the architect—for not obtaining a proper structure without fault or failure, although the architect's subcontractors are often included in any claim for damages and liability. The construction contractor, if he can prove normal care and compliance with standard trade practice, is often freed from responsibility for the results of his operation. White[198] expressed the opinion that there will be an increasing tendency to find architects and engineers liable for injuries to third parties resulting from professional negligence.

Victor O. Schinnerer, a professional liability insurance consultant* for architectural and engineering groups in the United States, has gathered data on judgments obtained by owners and by third parties in cases involving professional liability. His findings suggest that:

1. "Privity of contract"—the concept that architects and engineers are considered to have legal responsibility only to the owner who engaged them—is no longer the recognized rule.

2. Errors of judgment can no longer be used as a defense.

Some examples, taken from information furnished by Mr. Schinnerer, may best illustrate the trend of legal action to be expected from

---

* Professional liability insurance became available from Lloyds of London only about 13 years ago. Since 1956, coverage as arranged through joint efforts of architectural and engineering societies in the United States has been available from the Continental Casualty Company, and since 1963 from the Travelers Casualty Company. This policy covers the insured's liability for acts, errors, and omissions arising from the performance of professional services, within the limits of $25 and $500,000, with deductible amounts from $500.

In the contract for the construction of the New York Coliseum, on the suggestion of the writer, the architects included a clause requiring the contractor to provide insurance which protected the architect and his agents against all third party claims resulting from any operation or phase of work. This protection became of considerable value when the legal talent of the plaintiffs following the form failure incident described on p. 100 started suit against everyone connected with the project. In the ensuing litigation, the architects and engineers were not held liable.

failures, and it is evident that there is a marked increase in the number of claims against architects and engineers in recent years.

The design for a three-story concrete laboratory included a fill above the roof slab using a lightweight aggregate which expanded and pushed the parapet walls out. The court awarded a judgment of $22,400 against the architect on the argument that sufficient skill, knowledge, and judgment was expected of the architect so that if damage results from his work, he is liable.

When a boy fell off a rear stoop of an apartment house, the architect who designed the building 6 years prior to the accident was held liable "for his handiwork" in designing a structure that would permit such an accident, but was released by the court because of a legal defect in the complaint.

The architects who designed a hospital were held liable, with a judgment of $83,000 for the death of a workman, when a boiler blew up during the test. The contractor had failed to install a pressure valve properly shown on the architect's plans. The judge ruled that the architects are supposed to "snoop, pry, and prod" and should have discovered the omission of the safety valve.

Other cases cover the liability for errors in judgment in designing foundations and in choice of materials which did not serve the desired purpose, as well as errors in structural design, details, and dimensions.

In a California case, a third party action by a contractor against the architect claimed that lack of supervision by the latter resulted in the contractor's employees doing the wrong thing and therefore he suffered loss. This might easily be extended to the point where a contractor will sue the architect for losses from failures resulting from his own performance. This goes far beyond the normally expected responsibility for the sufficiency of a design and the professional right to use judgment. It becomes an insurance to the owner and to all third parties that the product will be produced without loss or harm. It is equivalent to asking a physician to guarantee success of all treatment or surgery.

There may be need soon for a meeting of all the phases of the construction industry to clarify the limits of responsibility for the several factors—project concept, design, detail, material production and assembly, construction direction, and supervision. If each does his job properly after hiring the necessary experience if he does not himself have it, and if each does not attempt to do the job of another, there is good likelihood of success and freedom from failure. Until such agreement is reached and becomes a part of all contracts, the result of failures is doubly significant. It is the most important duty of all professional groups to eliminate all causes of failure, otherwise the present status of legal responsibility will hinder professional development.

PREVENTION OF FAILURES

Structural failures have occurred at all times and in all types of work. Reasons for collapse are often determined after long investigation, but usually after interest in the incident has waned, and little publicity is given to the final report. The cause of minor incidents is seldom announced. As a result, recurrence of similar accidents and failures is too common, as the cases presented have shown. It is hoped that publicity of all failures will become more widespread, and both the engineering profession and the construction industry can learn by the mistakes of others and avoid such incidents in their future work.

Figure 8.1—Problem of adequate inspection and control is documented in this picture from the collection of ACI Committee 311. The building code in the city where this concrete was placed specifically prohibits addition of retempering water. Moreover, this particular job was being inspected by an agency retained for the purpose, and for certification of inspection the owner paid $0.50 more per yard for the concrete. Workers here are adding water to the truck mixer in direct violation of the local code.

The technical control bureau is a private organization set up to qualify projects for construction liability and damage insurance; its origin in Europe was spurred by serious construction accidents in the 1920's which led to intensive investigations of ways to control construction practices. Some European governments set up administrative controls, but the bureaucratic red tape slowed construction progress. The technical control bureau concept evolved as a practical way of maintaining standards of public safety while avoiding greater government control. It also minimizes the risks of insurance companies dealing in construction insurance.

In 1934, architects, engineers and contractors in Belgium, under the guidance of the late Gustave Magnel, created the Bureau de Controle pour le Securité de la Construction en Belgique (SECO). This bureau controls design and construction methods to prevent "incidents" and also determines their causes if any occur. The owner or the builder pays a fee ranging from 0.8 to 1.5 percent of the contract cost, and the SECO staff of more than 30 full time engineers reviews and approves structural design, choice of materials, field practices, soil testing, and other key phases of construction. On the basis of SECO's certificate of approval, insurance companies write policies that cover all risks of total or partial damage that might occur during construction and for a 10 year period after completion.

Insurance premiums on a SECO-certified job range from 0.45 to 1 percent. Complete coverage protects not only the owner but the contractor and architects and all their agents, subcontractors, and vendors. Such items as replacement and rehousing costs in event of a collapse are included; it also covers third party liability. In effect, sufficiency of design and performance in strict compliance with the design are guaranteed.

Two similar control bureaus, financed by insurance companies, appeared in France about the time of SECO's organization in Belgium. In the Netherlands, there is a specialized service bureau, STUVO, dealing with prestressed concrete.

Establishment of a comparable technical control system in the United States would have the following advantages in creating a "third force" outside of government to establish and enforce consistently high standards of design and construction:

1. It would unify the responsibility for control of a project.

2. More efficient use of trained construction personnel could be made. A trained inspector could be stationed on a job, or visit a

number of jobs on a coordinated schedule, rather than imposing sporadic interruptions in design office schedule when the engineer must perform job inspection.

3. Testing laboratory standards could be raised by abolishing price competition.

4. A direct financial motive for insuring good designs and conforming construction would be provided. Since the control bureau is tied in with an insurance plan which must pay off in cold cash in event of failure, motivation will be toward strictness of control, as for example in the high standards of inspection now maintained by fire insurance companies.

5. It provides a technical staff trained to see projects with fresh and unbiased viewpoint.

The technical control bureau would also establish a firm basis for financing thorough field inspection. Under present conditions these funds are too often inadequate, and it seems to be difficult for the engineer to secure proper compensation to do the kind of inspection job that should be performed.

It seems highly desirable that engineers, architects, and contractors in the United States should develop some system of control comparable to these that have proved effective in Europe. This may be the one best pathway toward the elimination of failures; recurring defects and collapses have shown that purely voluntary methods are not enough. Certainly if the construction industry is not willing to face up to this kind of improvement, it will have to bear the burden of ever-increasing governmental restriction in the interest of public welfare and safety.

Acknowledgments

The author wishes to express his appreciation for permission granted by the following individuals and organizations for the use of photographs:

ACI Committee 311—Figures 1.1, 3.12, 4.4, and 8.1
Concrete Construction—Figure 3.6
Engineering News-Record—Figure 6.3
Portland Cement Association—Figure 6.2
H. M. Racey—Figures 4.8, 4.9, and 4.10
Soiltest, Incorporated—Figure 7.2

References

1. "Study of Failures of Concrete Structure," *Bulletin,* American Railway Engineering Association, V. 20, No. 211, Nov. 1918, pp. 3-28.

2. Humphrey, Richard L., "The Successes and Failures of Cement Construction," (President's Annual Address to the National Association of Cement Users), *Proceedings,* ACI, V. 3, 1907, pp. 17-26.

3. Harper, R. F., *Code of Hammurabi,* University of Chicago Press, Chicago, 1921, p. 83 ff.

4. Data for the summary appeared in the *Schweizerische Bauzeitung,* V. 24, 1894, p. 166 and V. 29, 1897, pp. 6-7. All of Stowell's reports appeared in the *Railroad Gazette* during the period 1878-1895; a scrapbook compiled by Thomas J. Long containing much of this information is also in the files of the Engineering Societies Library in New York.

5. Editorial, *Engineering News,* V. 49, No. 15, Apr. 9, 1903, p. 324.

6. "The Lesson From Recent Failures of Reinforced Concrete Structures," *Engineering News,* V. 56, No. 22, Nov. 29, 1906, p. 573.

7. Godfrey, Edward, *Engineering Failures and Their Lessons,* published by the author, Pittsburgh, 1924, 270 pp.

8. Lossier, Henry, *LaPathologie du Beton Arme,* Dunod, Paris, 1952, 100 pp. (A 1955 edition was translated into English by the Canadian National Research Council as "Pathology and Therapeutics of Reinforced Concrete," *Technical Translation* 1008, Ottawa, 1962.)

9. Hammond, Rolt, *Engineering Structural Failures,* Odhams Press, Ltd., London, 1956; Philosophical Library, New York, 1957, 224 pp.

10. Szechy, C., *Foundation Failures* (translated from the Hungarian), Concrete Publications, Ltd., London, 1961, 146 pp.

11. Champion, S., *Failure and Repair of Concrete Structures,* Contractors Record, Ltd., London, and John Wiley and Sons, Inc., New York, 1961, 199 pp.

12. McKaig, Thomas H., *Building Failures,* McGraw Hill Book Co., New York, 1962, 261 pp.

13. Feld, Jacob, "Difficulties and Incidents in Prestressed Concrete," *Journal,* Boston Society of Civil Engineers, Jan. 1964, pp. 54-74.

14. Mall, Günter, *Bauschäden; Ursache, Auswirkung, Verhütung* (Building Deterioration; Cause, Effect, Prevention), Bauverlag GmbH, Wiesbaden, 1963, 567 pp.

15. *The Engineer,* V. 92, 1901, p. 167.

16. *American Architect,* V. 73, 1901, p. 17.

17. Hawgood, H., "The Collapse of the Bixby Hotel at Long Beach, Calif., on Nov. 9," *Engineering News,* V. 56, No. 22, Nov. 29, 1906, pp. 555-558.

18. "Additional Notes on the Failure of the Bixby Hotel at Long Beach," *Engineering News,* V. 56, No. 23, Dec. 6, 1906, p. 599.

19. Letter to Editor, *Engineering News,* V. 57, No. 2, Jan. 10, 1907, p. 44.

20. "Failure of a Reinforced-Concrete Building, Detroit, Mich.," *Engineering News,* V. 69, No. 2, Jan. 9, 1913, p. 86.

21. "Building Failure Due to Workmanship," *Concrete-Cement Age,* V. 1, No. 6, Dec. 1912, pp. 99-100.

22. Rogers, Paul, discussion of "Failures of Concrete Structures," by Jacob Feld, ACI JOURNAL, *Proceedings* V. 54, No. 12, June 1958, p. 1208.

23. Anderson, Boyd G., "Rigid Frame Failures," ACI JOURNAL, *Proceedings* V. 53, No. 7, Jan. 1957, pp. 625-636.

24. Lunoe, Reinhart R., and Willis, George A., "Application of Steel Strap Reinforcement to Girders of Rigid Frames, Special AMC Warehouses," ACI JOURNAL, *Proceedings* V. 53, No. 7, Jan. 1957, pp. 669-678.

25. Elstner, Richard C., and Hognestad, Eivind, "Laboratory Investigation of Rigid Frame Failure," ACI JOURNAL, *Proceedings* V. 53, No. 7, Jan. 1957, pp. 637-668.

26. "Rigid Frame Failures Analyzed," ACI JOURNAL, *News Letter,* Apr. 1956, p. 34.

27. Cohen, Edward, "Rigid Frame Failure," *Civil Engineering*, V. 26, No. 2, Feb. 1956, pp. 45-50.

28. "Concrete Block Laid on Floor Slab, Jacked Columns to Form Roof," *Engineering News-Record*, V. 148, No. 8, Feb. 21, 1952.

29. "Waffle Block Roof Crashes," *Engineering News-Record*, V. 148, No. 13, Mar. 27, 1952.

30. "Jack Drop Causes Waffle Block Crash," *Engineering News-Record*, V. 148, No. 14, Apr. 3, 1952, p. 29.

31. "Waffle Roof Falls Again," *Engineering News-Record*, V. 148, No. 21, May 22, 1952, p. 25.

32. Seelye, Elwyn E., (letter), *Engineering News-Record*, V. 149, No. 17, Oct. 23, 1952, pp. 10, 15.

33. "Flat Slab Breaks From Columns in Building Failure," *Engineering News-Record*, V. 157, No. 15, Oct. 11, 1956, pp. 24-25.

34. "Experts Probe Building Failure," *Construction Methods*, V. 38, No. 11, Nov. 1956, p. 59.

35. "Opportunity Missed" (editorial), *Engineering News-Record*, V. 159, No. 24, Dec. 11, 1957, p. 156.

36. "Construction Failure at Jackson, Michigan," *Concrete Construction*, Dec. 1956, p. 5.

37. "Folded-Plate Concrete Roof Collapses; Reason Unknown," *Engineering News-Record*, V. 162, No. 9, Mar. 5, 1959, p. 23.

38. "Building Collapse Kills Five," *Engineering News-Record*, V. 165, No. 22, Dec. 1, 1960, p. 30.

39. "Collapse Blamed on Bearing Failures," *Engineering News-Record*, V. 165, No. 24, Dec. 15, 1960, p. 28.

40. "Erection Methods Blamed for Collapse," *Engineering News-Record*, V. 167, No. 5, Aug. 3, 1961, p. 22.

41. "Failure of a Reinforced Concrete Floor Under Test at Trenton, N.J.," *Engineering News*, V. 50, No. 25, Dec. 17, 1903, p. 553.

42. "School Roof Collapses, Inquiries Under Way," *Engineering News-Record*, V. 157, No. 12, Sept. 20, 1956, p. 27.

43. Prestressed Concrete Institute press releases, one undated received June 24, 1957, and the other dated Oct. 9, 1956.

44. Mensch, L. J., "Pitfalls in Store for Builders of Large Tanks," *Civil Engineering*, V. 25, No. 11, Nov. 1955, p. 64.

45. Vandegrift, L. E., "Some Failures of Reinforced Concrete Storage Bins," ACI JOURNAL, *Proceedings* V. 51, No. 4, Dec. 1954, pp. 353-360.

46. Blanks, Robert F., "Concreting for Prestressing," *Proceedings* Massachusetts Institute of Technology Conference on Prestressed Concrete, 1951, p. 136.

47. "Final Report of the Joint Committee on Concrete and Reinforced Concrete," *Proceedings*, ACI, V. 13, 1917, pp. 509-566.

48. Dreyer, Walter, discussion of "Stresses in Reinforced Concrete Due to Volume Changes," by C. P. Vetter, *Transactions*, ASCE, V. 98, 1933, pp. 1058-1059.

49. Vetter, C. P., "Stresses in Reinforced Concrete Due to Volume Changes," *Transactions*, ASCE, V. 98, 1933, pp. 1039-1053.

50. See pp. 8-10 of Reference 1.

51. See pp. 10-12 of Reference 1.

52. *Engineering News-Record*, Dec. 1, 1955, p. 96.

53. "Failure of Concrete Rigid Frame Blamed on Reinforcing Details," *Engineering News-Record*, Nov. 11, 1954, p. 36.

54. Balog, Louis, discussion of "Failures of Concrete Structures" by Jacob Feld, ACI JOURNAL, *Proceedings* V. 54, No. 12, June 1958, pp. 1198-1200.

55. "Careless Dimensioning Fells a Concrete Wall," *Engineering News-Record*, V. 146, No. 6, Feb. 8, 1951, p. 51.

56. "Tracer's Mistake Caused Concrete Wall Break at Sacramento," *Engineering News-Record*, V. 93, No. 10, Sept. 4, 1924, p. 375.

57. *Technical Paper* No. 99, Division of Building Research, National Research Council of Canada.

58. *Engineering News-Record*, V. 163, No. 16, Oct. 19, 1959, p. 19.

59. "Builders Arrested After Collapse," *Engineering News-Record*, Sept. 24, 1959, p. 30.

60. "Long Sentences Meted Out in Italian Building Collapse," *Engineering News-Record*, Nov. 3, 1960, p. 28.

61. Tuttle, M. C., Letter to Editor, *Engineering News*, V. 67, No. 1, Jan. 4, 1912.

62. See pp. 16-18 of Reference 1.

63. "The Collapse of a Reinforced Concrete Building Near Rochester, N.Y.," *Engineering Record*, V. 55, No. 1, Jan. 5, 1907, pp. 11-12.

64. *Engineering News:* V. 56, No. 22, Nov. 29, 1906, p. 577; V. 57, No. 1, Jan. 3, 1907, p. 1.

65. *Engineering News*, V. 57, No. 5, Jan. 31, 1907, p. 130.

66. "Failure of Reinforced-Concrete Building Under Construction, Indianapolis, Ind.," *Engineering News*, V. 66, No. 24, Dec. 14, 1911, p. 717.

67. Condron, T. L., "The Collapse of the Reinforced Concrete Building for the Prest-O-Lite Co. Under Construction at Indianapolis, Ind.," *Engineering News*, V. 66, No. 25, Dec. 28, 1911, pp. 780-782. Also a continuation of this article in V. 67, No. 2, Jan. 11, 1912, pp. 66-69.

68. *Engineering News*, V. 67, No. 12, Mar. 21, 1912, p. 547.

69. "Concrete Hotel Building Collapse After Cold Weather," *Engineering News*, V. 95, No. 20, Nov. 12, 1925, pp. 800-801.

70. "Failure of Concrete-Steel Building at Corning, N.Y.," *Engineering News*, V. 51, No. 4, Jan. 28, 1904, p. 82.

71. "A Collapsed Concrete-Steel Building," *Engineering News*, V. 51, No. 1, Jan. 7, 1904, p. 21.

72. *Engineering News*, V. 64, No. 21, Nov. 24, 1910, p. 582.

73. "The Collapse of the Reinforced-Concrete Henke Building, Cleveland, Ohio," *Engineering News*, V. 64, No. 23, Dec. 8, 1910, pp. 636-637.

74. Editorial, *Engineering News*, V. 65, No. 4, Jan. 26, 1911, p. 105.

75. Godfrey, Edward, letter to editor, *Engineering News*, V. 65, No. 4, Jan. 26, 1911, p. 108.

76. "Report of the Commission Appointed to Investigate the Collapse of the Henke Reinforced Concrete Building, Cleveland, O.," *Engineering News*, V. 65, No. 4, Jan. 26, 1911, p. 117.

77. Turner, C. A. P., letter to editor, *Engineering News*, V. 65, No. 8, Feb. 23, 1911, p. 236.

78. Saurbrey, Alexis, "Further Notes on Collapse of the Henke Reinforced-Concrete Building," *Engineering News*, V. 65, No. 8, Feb. 23, 1911, p. 238.

79. "Careless Work Causes Concrete Bridge Failure," *Engineering News*, V. 76, No. 14, Oct. 5, 1916, p. 672.

80. "Poor Concrete in Columns Caused Failure of Bridge," *Engineering Record*, V. 74, Nov. 11, 1916, p. 597.

81. "Concrete Building Collapses, Killing 3," *Engineering News-Record*, V. 151, No. 3, July 16, 1953, p. 26.

82. "Defects Found in Building That Failed," *Engineering News-Record*, V. 151, No. 21, Nov. 19, 1953, p. 26.

83. "Engineers Report on Possible Causes of Building Failure at Scarsdale, N.Y.," *Engineering News-Record*, V. 151, No. 22, Nov. 26, 1953, p. 22; also editorial, p. 84, "Competent Inspection Is the Lesson."

84. Howe, Warner, "Can The Engineering Contract Cover Detail Engineering Costs?" *Consulting Engineer*, V. 15, No. 1, July 1960 pp. 86-88.

85. "A Plea for Supervision," *Engineering News-Record*, V. 162, No. 9, Mar. 5, 1959, p. 104.

86. *Engineering Record*, V. 74, No. 5, July 29, 1916, p. 151.

87. "Bad Concrete Halts Columbia Project," *New York Times*, Aug. 31, 1963, p. 19.

88. "Concrete Testing Is Called Unsafe," *New York Times*, July 17, 1963, p. 33.

89. See Reference 1, pp. 18-19.

90. "Concrete Arch Rib Fails Due to Laitance at Joint," *Engineering News-Record*, V. 90, No. 8, Feb. 22, 1923, p. 355.

91. "State Closes Rough Riding Expressway," *Engineering News-Record*, V. 165, No. 4, July 28, 1960, p. 22.

92. Feld, Jacob, "Strength of Precast Concrete Floor Joists," ACI JOURNAL, *Proceedings* V. 45, No. 2, Oct. 1948, pp. 141-148.

93. "Defects Delay Job," *Engineering News-Record*, V. 160, No. 8, Feb. 20, 1958, p. 24.

94. "The Reinforced Concrete Bath House Failure at Atlantic City, N.J.," *Engineering News,* V. 55, No. 14, Apr. 5, 1906, p. 396.

95. Eckert, Otto, "Frozen Concrete Responsible for Building Collapse," *Engineering Record,* V. 71, No. 9, Feb. 27, 1915, p. 271.

96. Stenger, Clifford M., "Failure of a Reinforced-Concrete Theater in Course of Construction, Cincinnati, Ohio," *Engineering News,* V. 68, No. 26, Dec. 26, 1912, pp. 1233-1235.

97. Condron, T. L., "Reinforced Concrete Hotel Under Construction Fails By Progressive Collapse," *Engineering News-Record,* V. 92, No. 6, Feb. 7, 1924, pp. 239-242.

98. "Further Data on Benton Harbor Concrete Building Failure," *Engineering News-Record,* V. 92, No. 14, Apr. 3, 1924, pp. 556-559.

99. Racey, H. J., "Lessons from Cold-Weather Concrete Failures," *Civil Engineering,* Nov. 1957, pp. 57-59.

100. Racey, H. J., "Winter Concreting With Particular Reference to Building Structures," unpublished address before American Concrete Institute Meeting, Montreal, P. Q., Oct. 25, 1956.

101. ACI Committee 604, "Recommended Practice for Winter Concreting (ACI 604-56)," ACI JOURNAL, *Proceedings* V. 52, No. 10, June 1956, pp. 1025-1047 (reprinted in *ACI Book of Standards*).

102. ACI Committee 605, "Recommended Practice for Hot Weather Concreting (ACI 605-59)," reprinted in *ACI Book of Standards,* American Concrete Institute, Detroit, Mich., 10 pp.

103. "Cooked Concrete," *Engineering News-Record,* July 12, 1962, p. 92.

104. Morrison, W. G., "New Zealand Completes First Major Prestressed Bridge," *Civil Engineering,* Nov. 1955, p. 64.

105. Factories Act (Great Britain) 1961, S.I. 1961, No. 1580, The Construction (General Provisions) Regulations, 1961.

106. Short, W. D., "Accidents on Construction Work With Special Reference to Failures During Erection or Demolition," *The Structural Engineer* (London), Feb. 1962, pp. 35-43.

107. "This Lift Slab Collapsed When These Pipe Columns Failed," *Engineering News-Record,* V. 153, No. 5, July 29, 1954, p. 25.

108. "Lift Slab Damages," *Engineering News-Record,* V. 157, No. 22, Nov. 29, 1956, p. 27.

109. "Wind Tilts Lift Slab Garage," *Engineering News-Record,* V. 156, No. 16, Apr. 19, 1956, p. 25.

110. "Plumbing Tilted Garage," *Engineering News-Record,* V. 156, No. 18, May 3, 1956, p. 25.

111. See p. 23 of Reference 1.

112. *Engineering News,* V. 50, No. 25, Dec. 17, 1903, p. 554; also No. 26, Dec. 24, 1903, p. 578.

113. ACI Committee 347, "ACI Standard Recommended Practice for Concrete Formwork (ACI 347-63)," American Concrete Institute, Detroit, 1963.

114. "Reservoir Roof Formwork Collapses Under Pouring Load," *Construction Methods*, V. 31, No. 5, May 1949, p. 48.

115. "Forms Fail, Floor Falls; 15 Workers Are Injured," *Engineering News-Record*, V. 142, No. 25, June 23, 1949, p. 36.

116. "Concrete Tank Roof Failure Probed," *Engineering News-Record*, V. 151, No. 16, Oct. 15, 1953, p. 25.

117. "Inquiry Clears N.Y. Coliseum Builders," *Civil Engineering*, V. 25, No. 8, Aug. 1955, p. 526.

118. "N.Y. Coliseum Floor Collapses During Construction," *Civil Engineering*, V. 25, No. 6, June 1955, p. 83.

119. "Formwork Failure Findings," *Engineering News-Record*, July 14, 1955, p. 23.

120. "Falsework Failure Injures Eleven Men," *Engineering News-Record*, Oct. 11, 1956, p. 25.

121. "Montreal Factory Roof Collapses," *Engineering News-Record*, Nov. 12, 1959, p. 29.

122. *Engineering News-Record*, V. 163, No. 21, Nov. 19, 1959, p. 41.

123. "Form Collapse in Atlanta Kills Worker," *Engineering News-Record*, V. 163, No. 10, Sept. 3, 1959, p. 23.

124. "Calls Strike as Cave-In Injures 15," *Detroit News*, Aug. 29, 1959, p. A 3.

125. "Recommended Standard Safety Code for Vertical Shoring," Steel Scaffolding and Shoring Institute, Cleveland, 1963, 16 pp.

126. "Jury Blames TTC, Firms for Cave-In," *Globe and Mail* (Toronto), July 7, 1961, p. 1.

127. "Designs Inadequate, Engineer Tells Probe Into Subway Deaths," *Globe and Mail* (Toronto), July 6, 1961, p. 11.

128. "Fatal Form Collapse Laid to Improper Bracing," *Engineering News-Record*, Aug. 10, 1961, pp. 26-27.

129. "Puzzling Failure," *Engineering News-Record*, V. 159, No. 20, Nov. 21, 1957, p. 15.

130. "Tank Roof Falls; Four Die; Suspect Faulty Formwork," *Engineering News-Record*, V. 169, No. 25, Dec. 20, 1962, p. 49.

131. "Collapse of Tank Dome Formwork," *Engineering News-Record*, V. 170, No. 2, Jan. 10, 1963, p. 20.

132. "Finished Concrete," *Engineering News-Record*, May 18, 1961, p. 31.

133. "250-Ft. Concrete Arch Across Spokane River Collapses During Construction," *Engineering News*, V. 77, No. 7, Feb. 15, 1917, p. 292.

134. "Report on Collapse of Falsework on Spokane Concrete Bridge," *Engineering News*, V. 77, No. 8, Feb. 22, 1917, pp. 314-316.

135. "Failure of the Roof of a Reinforced Concrete Building, Winnipeg, Man.," *Engineering News*, V. 66, No. 14, Oct. 5, 1911, p. 408.

136. "Failure of a Concrete Floor at Chicago," *Engineering News*, V. 48, No. 23, Dec. 4, 1902, p. 478.

137. *Engineering News,* V. 58, No. 3, July 18, 1907, p. 69.

138. Lyman, R. R., "Reinforced Concrete Roof Collapses," *Engineering Record,* V. 70, No. 1, July 4, 1914, p. 24.

139. "Collapse Delays Garage Job," *Engineering News-Record,* V. 164, No. 11, March 17, 1960, p. 23.

140. "Collapse Probe Brings Indictments," *Engineering News-Record,* Feb. 9, 1961, p. 28.

141. "Hunt 4 Lost in Rocket Cell Cave-In," *Detroit News,* Dec. 18, 1962, p. 1.

142. "Collapse Clues Sought in Test Silo," *Engineering News-Record,* Jan. 3, 1963, p. 15.

143. "Inflated Bag Forms Let It Down," *Engineering News-Record,* V. 131, No. 24, Dec. 2, 1943, p. 55.

144. "More Data on Concrete Dome Building Collapse," *Engineering News-Record,* V. 131, No. 25, Dec. 16, 1963, p. 69.

145. "Air-Supported Vinyl Form . . . Falls During Concreting," *Engineering News-Record,* June 21, 1962, p. 44.

146. Hurd, M. K., *Formwork for Concrete,* American Concrete Institute Detroit, 1963, 339 pp.

147. ACI Committee 201, "Durability of Concrete in Service," ACI JOURNAL, *Proceedings* V. 59, No. 12, Dec. 1962, pp. 1771-1820.

148. Brazier, who was a professor at the University of Aberdeen, reported on the Aberdeen Harbor dock in 1882 or 1883. His study is cited on p. 7 of Reference 1.

149. Vicat, M., *Proceedings* Institution of Civil Engineers (London), V. 16, Session 1856-57, p. 440.

150. Tyler, I. L., "Long-Time Study of Cement Performance in Concrete: Chapter 12, Concrete Exposed to Sea Water and Fresh Water," ACI JOURNAL, *Proceedings* V. 56, No. 9, Mar. 1960, pp. 825-836.

151. Halstead, S., and Woodworth, L. A. "The Deterioration of Reinforced Concrete Structures Under Coastal Conditions," *Transactions,* South African Institution of Civil Engineers, V. 5, No. 4, Apr. 1955, pp. 115-134.

152. "Ocean Pier to Be Scrapped Because of Concrete Disintegration," *Engineering News-Record,* V. 84, No. 13, Mar. 25, 1920, p. 621.

153. Sea Action Committee of the Institution of Civil Engineers (England), "The Durability of Reinforced Concrete in Sea Water," National Building Studies, *Research Paper* No. 30, 1960, H.M.S.O., London.

154. South African Council for Scientific and Industrial Research, *Corrosion of Concrete Sewers,* Wallach's P. and P. Co., Ltd., Pretoria, 1959, 236 pp.

155. Swab, Bernal H., "Effects of Hydrogen Sulfide on Concrete Structures," *Journal of the Sanitary Division, Proceedings,* ASCE, V. 87, SA 5, Sept. 1961, 15 pp.

156. "Tests of Form Lumber and Form Oil," *Miscellaneous Paper* No. 6-80, Mar. 1954, U.S. Army Corps of Engineers, Waterways Experiment Station, Vicksburg, Miss.

157. Feld, Jacob, "Diagnosis of Distress and Failure in Structures," *Journal, Engineering Institute of Canada*, (Montreal), Sept. 1963.

158. "A Concrete Floor in Candy Factory (JPP 35-6)," ACI JOURNAL, *Proceedings* V. 35, No. 2, Nov. 1938, p. 116.

159. Shermer, Carl L., "Corroded Reinforcement Destroys Concrete Beams," *Civil Engineering*, V. 26, No. 12, pp. 56-57.

160. "Liability of Reinforced Concrete to Electrolytic Damage," *Engineering News*, V. 57, No. 12, Mar. 21, 1907, p. 329.

161. Brown, Harold P., "Serious Injury to a Reinforced Concrete Building by Electrolysis," *Engineering News*, V. 65, No. 23, June 8, 1911, pp. 684-687.

162. McCroery, Don Hull, "Electrolysis and Corrosion Damage Warehouse," *Civil Engineering*, V. 4, No. 11, Nov. 1934, pp. 572-575.

163. Monfore, G. E., and Verbeck, G. J., "Corrosion of Prestressed Wire in Concrete," ACI JOURNAL, *Proceedings* V. 57, No. 5, Nov. 1960, pp. 491-515.

164. Trahern, J. W., "Prestressed Concrete Tanks—Design, Construction, Maintenance," *Symposium on Concrete Construction in Aqueous Environments*, Special Publication No. 8, American Concrete Institute, Detroit, 1964, pp. 43-54.

165. "Wires Break in Prestressed Reservoir," *Engineering News-Record*, V. 154, No. 22, June, 1955, p. 27.

166. "103-ft Sludge Tank Collapses," *Engineering News-Record*, May 4, 1961, p. 23.

167. "Corrosion Wrecked Prestressed Tank," *Engineering News-Record*, Nov. 2, 1961, pp. 23-24.

168. Schupak, M., "Prestressed Concrete Tank Performance," *Symposium on Concrete Construction in Aqueous Environments*, Special Publication No. 8, American Concrete Institute, Detroit, 1964, pp. 55-66.

169. Feld, Jacob, "Lessons from Structural Failures," *The 78th Annual Report*, Connecticut Society of Civil Engineers, 1962, pp. I-120 to I-147.

170. Klock, Morgan B., and Sheridan, Robert R., "Study of Shrinkage in Concrete Frames," ACI JOURNAL, *Proceedings* V. 53, No. 8, Feb. 1957, pp. 791-796.

171. Feld, Jacob, "Study of Dusty Concrete Ceilings," ACI JOURNAL, *Proceedings* V. 45, No. 9, May 1949, pp. 673-680.

172. "Spalled Concrete Traced to Conduit," *Engineering News-Record*, V. 172, No. 11, Mar. 12, 1964, pp. 28-29.

173. "Collapse of the Ireland Building," *Engineering Record*, V. 32, No. 14, Aug. 31, 1895, p. 244.

174. Merrill, John O., "Foundation Caused Collapse of Old Chicago Club Building," *Engineering News-Record*, V. 101, No. 19, Nov. 8, 1928, pp. 692-693.

175. See p. 4 of Reference 1.

176. "The Collapse of the Darlington Apartment House in New York City," *Engineering News*, V. 51, No. 10, Mar. 10, 1904, pp. 217-219.

177. Sée, Paul, "Unforeseen Accidents," *Memoires de la Société des Ingenieurs Civils de France* (Paris), March 1907.

178. "Shoddy Work Caused Building Failure," *Engineering News-Record*, Apr. 25, 1946, p. 675.

179. "Building Collapse Laid to Careless Underpinning," *Engineering News-Record*, V. 158, No. 19, May 9, 1957, p. 75.

180. "Building Failures Alarm Rio," *Engineering News-Record*, V. 159, No. 6, Aug. 8, 1957, p. 51.

181. Reitz, Henry M., Letter to Editor, *Concrete Construction*, Jan. 1964, pp. 20-21.

182. "Soil Settlement Imperils Buildings," *Engineering News-Record*, V. 157, No. 15, Oct. 11, 1956, p. 33.

183. "Anchorage Slip Wrecks Suspension Bridge," *Engineering News-Record*, V. 159, No. 17, Oct. 24, 1957.

184. "Lost Gamble," *Engineering News-Record*, V. 165, No. 22, Dec. 1, 1960, p. 25.

185. "Shale Scuttles Reservoir Design," *Engineering News-Record*, July 28, 1960, pp. 41-42.

186. "11 Story Building Turns Over," *Engineering News-Record*, V. 160, No. 17, Feb. 13, 1958, p. 44.

187. See p. 14 of Reference 1.

188. "Wall Failure Proves Expensive," *Engineering News-Record*, V. 161, No. 19, Nov. 6, 1958, p. 23.

189. Armstrong, James W., "Failure of Dividing Wall in Old Coagulation Basin of Baltimore Water Filtration Plant," *Engineering News-Record*, V. 102, No. 15, Apr. 11, 1929, pp. 597-599.

190. Feld, Jacob, "Structural Success or Failure?" *Proceedings* ASCE, V. 81, Separate No. 632, Feb. 1955, 13 pp.

191. Mather, Bryant, discussion of "Structural Success or Failure?" by Jacob Feld, *Proceedings* ASCE, V. 81, Paper No. 758, pp. 758-5 and 758-6.

192. See p. 13 of Reference 1.

193. See p. 12 of Reference 1.

194. "Righting a Tilted Grain Elevator," *Engineering News*, V. 72, No. 9, Aug. 27, 1914, pp. 464-468.

195. "Mudjacking Saves a Grain Elevator," *Engineering News-Record*, Sept. 15, 1955.

196. "Was It an Explosion or a Foundation Failure?" *Engineering News-Record*, June 23, 1955, p. 27.

197. Peck, Charles F., Jr., "Philadelphia Explosion," *Engineering News-Record*, May 17, 1956, p. 8.

198. White, George M., "Architects' and Engineers' Third Party Negligence Liability—The Fall of the House of Privity," *Western Reserve Law Review*, Sept. 1959.

199. "Saving Money on Inspection?" *Engineering News-Record*, V. 171, No. 12, Sept, 19, 1963, p. 290.

200. "Penalty for Bad Work," *Engineering News-Record*, V. 171, No. 9, Aug. 29, 1963, p. 72.

Index

171

QMW LIBRARY
(MILE END)